HARCOURT, BRACE SCIENCE PROGRAM

*Under the
General Editorship of
Paul F. Brandwein*

JUNIOR HIGH SCHOOL *Science for Better Living Series*

You and Your World
Teacher's Manual · Teaching Tests

You and Your Inheritance
Teacher's Manual · Teaching Tests

You and Science
Teacher's Manual · Teaching Tests, Forms A and B
Experiences in Science (Workbook) · Harbrace Science Filmstrips

Science for Better Living: Complete Course
Teaching Tests · Film Guide

SENIOR HIGH SCHOOL

Exploring Biology: Fourth Edition
Teacher's Sourcebook · Teaching Tests, Forms A and B
Experiences in Biology

Your Biology
Teacher's Manual (Including Unit Tests)

Your Health and Safety: Fourth Edition
Teacher's Manual · Teaching Tests

The Physical World: A Course in Physical Science
Teacher's Manual · Teaching Tests

Exploring Chemistry (In Preparation)
Teacher's Manual · Teaching Tests · *Experiences in Chemistry*

Exploring Physics
Experiences in Physics

A SPECIAL BOOK FOR THE STUDENT
● **How To Do an Experiment**

BOOKS FOR THE TEACHER
Teaching High School Science: A Book of Methods
Teaching High School Science: A Sourcebook for the Biological Sciences
Teaching High School Science: A Sourcebook for the Physical Sciences
(In Preparation)

HOW TO DO
AN EXPERIMENT

Philip Goldstein

Chairman, Department of Biology
Abraham Lincoln High School
Brooklyn, New York

UNDER THE GENERAL EDITORSHIP OF
Paul F. Brandwein

HARCOURT, BRACE AND COMPANY

NEW YORK · CHICAGO

Dedication

When I look back at my college years, I am somewhat surprised that I remember so few of my former teachers. Evidently very few of my college professors made a lasting impression on me.

But there was one man who affected me profoundly. It was in his classes in Experimental Biology that I became infected with a love for science, and with an understanding of scientific method. Much of what I have put into this book is based on what I learned during my association with him.

Therefore, it is with the greatest of pleasure that I dedicate this book to Abram J. Goldforb, for a long time professor of biology at the College of the City of New York. This is one small way in which I can express my sincere thanks. It is my hope that in writing this book, I can pass along to younger students a little of the spark and spirit which Professor Goldforb kindled in me.

Philip Goldstein

Contents

50468

How can you get a start toward becoming a scientist?

1 The Purpose of This Book

Science can be a fascinating subject for most girls and boys. As its wonders unfold before their eyes, their minds are dazzled by the amazing discoveries which scientists have made. The scientists themselves and the spirit of discovery are glorified. At the same time, a serious shortage of scientists is proclaimed in newspapers throughout the nation. So it is not at all surprising that many young people want to become a part of the future of science. They visualize themselves in spotlessly clean, white laboratory coats, holding test tubes full of multi-colored fluids. They see themselves turning knobs and manipulating all sorts of elaborate apparatus. They dream of things boiling and bubbling and sizzling, and out of the confusion, a Nobel prize-winning discovery emerges.

But as the daydream passes over, many of these boys and girls begin to ask of themselves, "Can I really make a great discovery someday? Can I learn to experiment? Can I do an experiment now?"

The answer, of course, is yes! Actually, the hardest part is getting started. Once the initial difficulties are overcome, the rest goes easier. But getting started ——!!!

The purpose of this book is to help you get started. After you have read the book, you will not only understand better your school work in science; you will also have a clearer understanding of how to do an experiment. Perhaps it will stimulate you to begin an experiment of your own and carry it through to a successful conclusion. Maybe it will help you win a prize at a science fair, or in a competitive science scholarship. Possibly it will start you off on the road to a career in science. Best of all, *perhaps this book will give you a better understanding of the methods of science, and the ways in which you may use the methods of science to help solve your problems.*

2 The Methods of Science

Science has been defined in various ways, but most definitions agree that *science begins with the search for knowledge or truth.* If this is so, then obviously a scientist should set himself the task of finding the truth, and any method he uses to do this is a scientific method. A scientist is not bound by any special "scientific method." Rather, he feels free to use any and all methods or devices which are likely to give him the correct answer to the problem he is studying.

The *correct* answer — this is what the scientist is after. But how does one know if an answer is correct? Logically, there must be some way of checking, and this is one of the characteristics of scientific truth. It is the type of truth which can be verified again and again. A scientist discovers some bit of knowledge. Before it is accepted as truth, it is tested and retested, checked and rechecked. If there is general agreement, the bit of knowledge is accepted as truth. It is not true because it is stated in a book, or because a great scientist says so. Nor is it true because history says so, or because society says it should be. It is true because it can be proved again and again by anyone who has the know-how and the desire to check it for himself.

Check it for yourself! One of the marks of a true scientist is his recognition that in all of his work there is something which needs checking — a problem, or a result. The scientist must recognize the problem and approach it objectively, without holding a fixed notion of what will happen. He must not be influenced by his social or economic views, or by what he hopes will happen. He must not let his personal or political beliefs obscure his clear view. With an unbiased mind, he must determine what method or methods will be most effective in getting an honest answer to the problem. He does not trust the view of his neighbor (not that he thinks his neighbor is dishonest); nor even his own first results (everybody makes mistakes). He checks and verifies, again and again. He publicizes his results, and hopes that when others recheck, they will show that his findings are substantially correct.

Although there is no single method by which scientists work, much of what science has discovered resulted from following a certain basic pattern of thought. There is nothing mysterious or secret in this pattern of thought, and you don't have to be a scientist to use it. As a matter of fact, we all use this method in one form or another in solving personal problems. Frequently our use of this thought pattern is completely automatic; many great contributions to human knowledge have been made by applying it unconsciously to various puzzling situations.

Remember that there really is no one scientific method, but rather that there are many scientific methods. People, however, have pinned the name, *The Scientific Method,* on a certain pattern of thinking which has helped make many scientific discoveries. This pattern is analyzed below.

1. Someone runs into a puzzling situation, and recognizes THE EXISTENCE OF A PROBLEM.

2. He studies the problem and gathers as much information about it as possible, in order to make complete THE ANALYSIS OF THE PROBLEM.

3. Now he makes one or more good guesses as to the answer to the problem. These guesses may be based on previous experience, or they may be plain hunches. The making of " educated " guesses is called THE FORMATION OF WORKING HYPOTHESES.

4. Finding the correct solution to the problem requires THE TESTING OF EACH HYPOTHESIS, as follows:

a. *Evidence is gathered* — by setting up and carrying out one or more appropriate experiments, by making a series of accurate observations, by assembling and organizing many isolated facts which are already known, or by using any other technique which will do the job.

b. *Two possibilities are considered for each hypothesis.* Either the evidence supports a hypothesis as a possible correct answer to the problem, or the evidence indicates that the hypothesis is not in keeping with the facts.

5. The results obtained by testing require THE ELIMINATION OR MODIFICATION OF WRONG OR FAULTY HYPOTHESES.

6. Any hypothesis which seems to be in keeping with the observed facts is accepted — at least for the time being — as a possible correct answer to the problem. The conditional acceptance of a hypothesis is called THE FORMATION OF A TENTATIVE CONCLUSION.

7. Further testing or experimentation, reference to the work of other scientists, and other means of evaluation are employed to accomplish THE CHECKING OF THE TENTATIVE CONCLUSION.

8. If the tentative conclusion fails to stand up, new working hypotheses are formed. If, on the other hand, the tentative conclusion continues to stand up, the result is THE ACCEPTANCE OF THE TENTATIVE CONCLUSION AS FACT.

9. The solution to the problem is made known to other scientists, who may use it as the starting point for related investigations or for adding another improvement to our way of living. THE USE OF THE NEW FACT, if only for knowledge's sake, is a good measure of the importance of the investigation.

Let us now see how the methods of science have helped in solving problems which arose at different times in history. The next chapter describes and analyzes three of these problems.

3 Using the Methods of Science to Solve Problems

Case One — What Is the True Shape of the Earth?

For many thousands of years people walked the surface of the earth, secure in their belief that the earth was flat. This belief was the logical result of their everyday observations, and it seemed to satisfy all the conditions of life. They walked on a flat surface, and wherever they looked, the flat earth stretched away in all directions as far as the eye could see.

However, as long ago as 530 B.C. someone dared to question the truth of what he saw with his eyes. A Greek mathematician named Pythagoras claimed that the earth was round like a sphere rather than flat like a saucer. This was his opinion, but he could not support it or prove it. In the third century B.C., another Greek named Eratosthenes actually measured the earth, and found it to be a sphere with a circumference of 25,000 miles.

Yet these strange views did not change the opinions of most people who lived during the next two thousand years. The established authorities continued to believe their eyes and accepted the view that the earth was flat. The average man continued to trust the views of the established authorities. But the idea that the earth was round kept turning up like a bad penny.

Toward the end of the fifteenth century, Christopher Columbus made some observations which led him to believe that the earth was actually a sphere, even though the view was quite unpopular at the time. Columbus realized that if his theory about the shape of the earth was correct, he could solve another important problem of the day — strictly a business problem.

In those days, Europeans traded with India and other Eastern countries for many valuable things such as silks and spices. They got to India by sailing *eastward* from Europe. However, the Turks gained control of all the eastern routes to India, and prevented other people from going there. This created a great shortage of all those things which India supplied, and anyone who could find a way of running the blockade could make a fortune for himself.

This was the problem which Columbus hoped to solve — if his theory concerning the shape of the earth was correct. If the earth was actually a sphere, India could be reached by sailing *westward* from Europe. It might take a little longer than going by the eastward route, but it was just as sure (Figure 1-a). However, if the earth were actually flat — and this was the view of most people of the time — then a westward trip might be disastrous (Figure 1-b).

Columbus finally managed to get some ships, assemble a crew, and set sail *westward*. He never succeeded in reaching India, however, because a continent which he did not know about got in his way. He accidentally discovered America (Figure 1-c).

When Columbus did not fall off the "edge of the world," more captains began to take their ships westward. Finally, the expedition headed by Ferdinand Magellan proved conclusively that the earth is round. Magellan's group of five ships and 230 men sailed westward from Spain in 1519. Magellan himself was killed during the trip, but one ship and about eighteen men managed to go all the way around the earth and back to Spain in 1522. This would have been impossible if the earth were flat.

Gradually, the view of the great majority changed as new evidence mounted. People were convinced that the earth is really round, even though it looks flat. As the belief that the earth is round became more and more established, the information was used to help discover other phenomena such as the path which the earth follows as it travels about the sun.

Perhaps you may feel that this is not science. You may ask what the voyage of Columbus had to do with scientific method. Yet the basic thought patterns were used by Columbus. He may not have been aware that he was using the methods of science, but, nevertheless, he used them effectively. Because he tested his hypothesis, the truth came out. If Columbus had not sailed westward and discovered a new continent, men like Magellan might have refrained for many years from setting out to sail around the world.

Analyze the summary below, and you will see clearly how the basic steps which are used in solving many science problems played a part in determining the true shape of the earth.

FIGURE 1. *Columbus' problem was finding a new route to India. Was there such a route?*

a. *If the earth is round —*

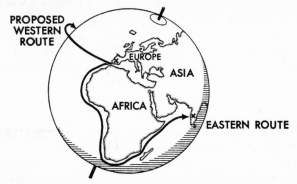

b. *If the earth is flat —*

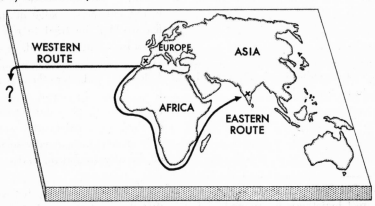

c. *Columbus' plan led him to discover America.*

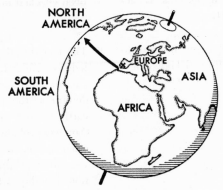

Summary

1. Observation leads people to formulate a hypothesis as to the shape of the earth.

1. The earth looks flat. Therefore people thought it was flat.

2. This view is questioned, and a different hypothesis is proposed.

2. Pythagoras thought that the earth was round like a sphere. Eratosthenes measured the size of the sphere.

3. People test the two opposing theories by observation and experiment.
Hypothesis A — the earth is flat
Hypothesis B — the earth is round

3. Based on his observations, Columbus guessed that he could reach India by sailing westward around the spherical earth.
   Other people claimed he would fall off the edge of the flat world if he tried to reach India by sailing westward.

4. One hypothesis is finally proved to be correct.

4. Columbus, and later others, performed the experiment of sailing westward. They did not fall off the "edge of the earth."
   Magellan's men actually sailed all the way around the earth.

5. After further testing, the incorrect hypothesis is dropped, and the correct hypothesis is accepted as fact.

5. Educated people today believe that the earth is round. It has been checked many times.

6. The new fact is put to work to help find additional knowledge.

6. The fact that the earth is round helps us understand the earth as part of the solar system and to determine the path which the earth follows around the sun. (You can probably think of many other problems to which men were able to apply the information that the earth is round.)

Case Two — Do Maggots Appear Spontaneously in Decaying Meat?

Now let us consider another important scientific discovery. Note that this discovery was made as far back as 1688. It is being cited here to show that there is nothing new about scientific methods.

For untold thousands of years, people believed that living things could arise spontaneously from non-living matter. They saw worms (maggots) appear in decaying meat; they discovered frogs coming out of the mud of a riverbank; they found vermin in dirt. Quite logically, they assumed that the worms were generated by the meat, the frogs by the mud, the vermin by the dirt.

However, some people were puzzled by these observations. They were not satisfied by what appeared to be the obvious solution. For example, Francesco Redi, a famous Italian physician of the seventeenth century, became interested in learning the truth about maggots in meat. Below, you will find a description of Redi's thoughts, theories, observations, experiments, and conclusions as he set them down in 1688. Basically, the description is in his own words, translated into English. However, a few changes have been made in wording to make the reading easier today, and some portions have been omitted.

There is a popular belief that the decay of a dead body, or the filth of any sort of decayed matter, causes worms to develop. Being desirous of finding the truth, I performed the following experiment:

At the beginning of June, I had three snakes killed, and as soon as they were dead I placed them in an open box to decay. Not long afterwards I saw that they were covered with worms. . . . These worms were intent on devouring the meat, increasing meanwhile in size, and from day to day they likewise increased in number. . . . After having consumed the meat, leaving only the bones intact, they all escaped through an opening in the box, and I was unable to discover their hiding place.

Being curious to know their fate, I again prepared three of the same snakes, which in three days were covered with small worms. . . . When the meat was all consumed, the worms eagerly sought an exit, but I had closed every opening. On the nineteenth day some of the worms stopped moving, as if they were asleep, and they appeared to shrink and gradually assume the shape of an egg. By the next day all the worms had assumed the egg shape . . . and then changed from soft to hard resembling the chrysalis formed by caterpillars, silkworms, and similar insects. . . . [Here he describes pupae of different kinds and colors.]

I placed these pupae separately in glass vessels, well covered with paper, and at the end of eight days every shell of the red pupae was broken, and out of each came a gray fly . . . which later turned brilliant green. . . . Some black pupae took fourteen days to produce large black flies striped with white. . . . Other black pupae took twenty-one days, and produced some curious flies never described to my knowledge by any historian. . . . [Here he describes these flies.]

I continued similar experiments with the raw and cooked flesh of the ox, the deer, the buffalo, the lion, the tiger, the dog, the lamb, the kid, the rabbit, and sometimes with the flesh of ducks, geese, hens, swallows. . . . Finally I experimented with different kinds of fish such as swordfish, tuna, eel, sole. . . . In every case . . . flies were hatched. . . . Almost always I saw that the decaying flesh . . . was covered not alone with worms, but with the eggs from which the worms were hatched. These eggs made me think of those deposits dropped by flies on meats. . . .

Having considered these things, I began to believe that all worms found in meat were derived directly from the droppings of flies, and not from the putrefaction of the meat. [Italics added.] I was still more convinced of this by the observation that before meat grew wormy, flies hovered over it of the same kind that later bred in it. Belief would be useless without the confirmation of an experiment. Therefore, in the middle of July I put a snake, some fish, some eels . . . and a slice of milk-fed veal in four large wide-mouthed flasks; and sealed them well. [See Figure 2-a.] I then filled four more flasks in the same way, only leaving these open. [See Figure 2-b.] It was not long before the meat and fish in the open vessels became wormy, and flies were seen entering and leaving at will. But in the closed flasks, I did not see a worm. . . . Outside on the paper cover there was now and then a deposit, or a maggot that eagerly sought for an opening by which to reach the food inside. . . .

Not content with these experiments, I tried many others at different seasons, using different vessels. . . .

I thought I had proved that the flesh of dead animals could not produce worms unless the eggs of live flies were deposited in it. However, my tests had been made with closed vessels in which air could not penetrate or circulate. To remove all doubt, I prepared a

a. *Do maggots appear spontaneously on dead meat? (Notice that the flasks are sealed.)*

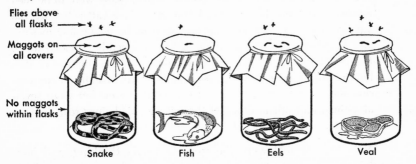

Flies above all flasks ⟶

Maggots on all covers

No maggots within flasks

Snake   Fish   Eels   Veal

b. *Or do they come to the meat from an outside source? (Notice that the flasks are not sealed.)*

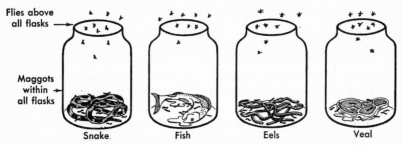

Flies above all flasks ⟶

Maggots within all flasks ⟶

Snake   Fish   Eels   Veal

FIGURE **3.** *Redi repeated his experiment — using a closed vase that was not airtight — to see whether the absence of air in the flasks he had sealed was responsible for the failure of maggots to develop. But again maggots appeared only on the cover.*

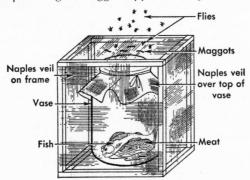

Flies

Maggots

Naples veil on frame

Naples veil over top of vase

Vase

Fish

Meat

17

new experiment by putting meat and fish in a large vase closed only with a fine Naples veil that allowed the air to enter. For further protection against flies, I placed the vessel in a frame covered with the same net. [See Figure 3.]

I never saw any worms in the meat, though many were to be seen moving about on the net-covered frame. These, attracted by the odor of the meat, succeeded at last in penetrating the fine meshes, and would have entered the vase had I not speedily removed them. It was interesting, in the meantime, to notice the number of flies buzzing about, which every now and then would light on the outside net and deposit eggs there. I noticed that some left six or seven at a time, and others dropped them in the air before reaching the net. . . .

Note how logical were the steps in Redi's thinking, and how simple and thorough were his observations and experiments. This is another example of scientific methods in action.

Summary

1. Common observations lead people to form a hypothesis as to the origin of maggots in meat.

1. " There is a popular belief that the decay of a dead body, or the filth of any sort of decayed matter, causes worms to develop." (Redi)

2. This view is questioned, and an opposing hypothesis is offered.

2. " Having considered these things [observations which he made] I began to believe that all worms found in meat were derived directly from the droppings of flies, and not from the putrefaction of the meat." (Redi)

3. This hypothesis is tested by observation and experiment.

3. " Belief would be useless without the confirmation of an experiment. Therefore in the middle of July . . ." Redi now set up his famous experiment with open and sealed flasks.

4. The test supports the tentative hypothesis.	4. "It was not long before the meat and fish in the open vessels became wormy . . . But in the closed flasks I did not see a worm." (Redi)
5. Further testing is carried out.	5. "Not content with these experiments, I tried many others at different seasons, using different vessels." (Redi)
6. A possible error arises.	6. "However, my tests had been made with closed vessels in which air could not penetrate or circulate." (Redi)
7. A special experiment is set up to check this possibility of error.	7. "To remove all doubt, I prepared a new experiment . . ." Redi now set up his famous experiment with a vase protected by netting.
8. The test still supports the conclusion.	8. "I never saw any worms in the meat . . ." (Redi)
9. The hypothesis is accepted as fact.	9. We know today that worms can only appear in meat upon which flies have laid eggs.
10. This information is applied to the solution of other problems.	10. Meat is protected against flies. Materials in which flies lay eggs are disposed of in a sanitary way.

This particular problem had an interesting history in the years that followed. Planned experiments like Redi's seemed to rule out the possibility of spontaneous generation, until Anthony van Leeuwenhoek discovered microorganisms. This reopened the question. Perhaps large organisms like maggots or mice or frogs were not generated spontaneously. But how about the tiny organisms — so tiny that they were beyond the imagination? How about bacteria, yeasts, and protozoa which seemed to appear out of nowhere in any decaying matter or any infusion? Here was a new hypothesis which needed testing, and scientists in every country got to work on the problem. This, however, is another story, and it might be well worthwhile for you to look up the work of some of these other scientists — men like Lazaro Spallanzani, John Tyndall, and Louis Pasteur. If you take the trouble to analyze the work of these men, you will see that they all followed the same basic pattern in their approach to the problem.

Case Three — How Could Unknown Planets in the Solar System Be Discovered?

The skies and the stars have always held a strong fascination for men. There is something mysterious and bewitching about the brilliant pinpoints of light which appear when darkness settles over the earth. Surely, this caused even the most primitive people to watch and to wonder. We find the heavenly bodies intimately tied up with ancient rites and religions, and with the folklore and myths of many former civilizations. It is small wonder that astronomy is considered to be the oldest of the sciences.

What is surprising is how much our ancestors were able to observe with the unaided eye. For example, the stargazers and astrologers of ancient days recognized the fact that among the heavenly bodies were some which differed from the rest. Without the use of telescopes or other optical equipment, they discovered and observed certain "wandering stars" which seemed to move, while other stars appeared to retain more or less fixed positions in constellations. These "wandering stars" were eventually identified as the planets Mercury, Venus, Mars, Jupiter, and Saturn.

It wasn't until 1609 that a telescope was turned on the heavens. In that year, Galileo pointed a small telescope (with lenses less than two inches in diameter) at the stars, and he was able to observe wonders which no one had ever seen before. He was able to see the mountains and the craters on the moon, the moons of Jupiter, the phases of Venus, and the ring around Saturn. This was the beginning of a new era in the study of the heavens.

Yet even with his telescope, Galileo was only able to see the same five planets which the ancients had discovered with the unaided eye — Mercury, Venus, Mars, Jupiter, and Saturn. In the years which followed, observations continued, and as telescopes became larger and better, more information was gathered about the heavenly bodies. Still, there was no reason for anyone to suspect that additional planets existed beyond Saturn.

Then, in 1781, William Herschel, an English astronomer, made a remarkable discovery. He was exploring a certain area of the sky with his telescope when he observed a heavenly body which seemed to be too large to be a star. Furthermore, this heavenly body was moving among the stars. Herschel recognized that this was a new planet, and it was named Uranus. Seven planets were now known — Mercury, Venus, Earth, Mars, Jupiter, Saturn, and Uranus. Astronomers studied the mass, the size, the density of these seven planets, and accumulated a great deal of data about them. Then, by applying certain laws of physics and mathematics to the known data, the path of each planet around the sun was calculated. Finally, careful observations were carried out all over the world to see whether the planets actually followed the calculated paths.

As a result of these observations, it was found that all the planets followed the expected paths around the sun except one — the newly discovered planet Uranus. Uranus swerved away from the calculated orbit at one point (Figure 4). Naturally, this led to the question, "Why does the actual orbit of Uranus differ from the calculated path?"

FIGURE **4.** *Of the seven planets known to man in 1800, only Uranus (the outermost of the seven) failed to follow the orbit calculated for it. Why did Uranus swing farther from the sun than was expected?*

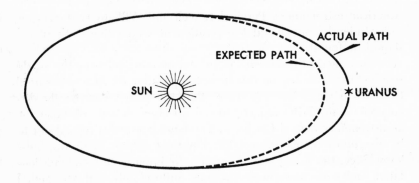

Of course, the most obvious theory was that the known facts about Uranus were not entirely correct. Another possibility was that an error had been made in calculating the path. But upon double checking, it turned out that there had been no errors of this sort. Finally, in 1846, Urbain J. J. Le Verrier, a French astronomer, and John C. Adams, an English astronomer, each independently proposed the hypothesis that there was another planet, as yet undiscovered, which was pulling Uranus off the expected course. Each of these men had made a series of mathematical calculations to prove that if another planet existed at a certain point in the sky, then Uranus would be pulled from the calculated course to its actual course.

Le Verrier urged the astronomers of the Berlin Observatory to examine the heavens at a certain point. The reason for selecting this observatory was that it had a very accurate star map of the particular area of the sky in question. Sure enough, they discovered there a new starlike object which was not recorded on the star map. This was planet number eight, and it was named Neptune. The hypothesis of Le Verrier and Adams, which had been worked out mathematically on paper, was verified by actual observation.

But the story does not end here. Even the discovery of the newest planet, Neptune, did not set everything right. The actual path of Uranus still swerved, ever so slightly, from the newly calculated path. Furthermore, the path followed by the newly discovered planet Neptune also swerved from the path that astronomers calculated for it! This led to the belief that there must be still another planet, as yet undiscovered, to account for these differences. In 1905, after carrying out involved mathematical calculations, two American astronomers, Percival Lowell and William H. Pickering, independently announced the position at which the ninth planet should be found.

Once again the search began. Astronomers all over the world scanned the skies around the indicated position. But it was not until twenty-five years later, in 1930, that the planet was finally discovered. A tiny, dim object showed up on a photograph taken by an astronomer named Clyde W. Tombaugh, and this turned out to be the ninth planet of our solar system — Pluto. With this new knowledge, the orbits of Uranus and Neptune were again recalculated, and were now found to agree quite closely with the actual paths followed by these planets.

Summary

1. Observation leads to an accumulation of knowledge.

1. (a) Ancient stargazers discovered a number of planets or "wandering stars."
(b) Galileo makes additional discoveries about these planets by using a telescope.
(c) Herschel discovers a new planet, Uranus, bringing the total number known to seven.
(d) The size, mass, and density of each planet are determined.

2. This knowledge is used to gain other information.

2. Based on physical laws, the expected orbit of each planet is calculated.

3. The new information is checked by further observation.

3. Every planet actually follows the expected course, except Uranus, which swerves off at one point.

4. A problem arises.

4. Why does the planet Uranus swerve off the expected course?

5. Several hypotheses are suggested.

5. (a) Our information about size, mass, and density of Uranus is incorrect.
(b) An error was made in calculating the path of Uranus.

6. These hypotheses are checked.

6. (a) The size, mass, and density of Uranus are refigured.
(b) The path of Uranus is recalculated.

7. These hypotheses are found to be incorrect and are eliminated.

7. (a) The data about Uranus are found to be correct.
(b) Based on these data, the path should be as calculated.

8. A new hypothesis is proposed.	8. Le Verrier and Adams suggest that there is another planet at point X which pulls Uranus off its calculated course.
9. This hypothesis is checked by observation.	9. Astronomers at the Berlin Observatory scan the sky at the point indicated and compare their observations with the star map of the region.
10. The hypothesis is shown to be correct.	10. A new planet, Neptune, is discovered at point X.
11. The new fact is used.	11. With the gravitational force of this new planet taken into consideration, the path of Uranus is recalculated.
12. A new problem arises.	12. The calculated path of Uranus is closer to the actual path, but it still does not agree.
13. A hypothesis is proposed.	13. Lowell and Pickering suggest that there is still another new planet to be found. They indicate where it should be.
14. This hypothesis is checked by observation.	14. Many astronomers study the sky at the point indicated.
15. The hypothesis is shown to be correct.	15. A new planet, Pluto, is discovered.
16. The new fact is used.	16. Once again, the orbits are recalculated. They are found to agree with the actual orbits.

You can see that no single science has a monopoly on scientific methods. Nor are scientific methods restricted to science alone. They can be used by anyone in everyday life, but they require knowledge, facts, and information. The next section of this book will be devoted to methods of obtaining information.

4 Reference to Authority

One of the easiest ways of finding the solution to a problem is to ask somebody who knows the answer. Such a person may be called an authority on the subject. For example, if you want to know the formula for the volume of a sphere, you might ask your mathematics teacher. He is an authority on mathematics and will be able to tell you that the volume of a sphere equals $\frac{4}{3}\pi r^3$.

A person is not the only kind of authority you can consult. You can go to a proper reference book of some sort. Thus, if your teacher asks you to make a class report on the conditions existing on the planet Mars, you will want to go to the library to locate this information. Naturally you will use the most authoritative books you can find on the subject because you want complete and accurate facts.

Reference to authority is a simple, convenient way of getting information, but it has certain definite drawbacks and limitations. For example, suppose you want to know the telephone number of your friend John Smith. You can call information and ask for the number, or you can refer to the telephone directory. In either case you are referring to an authoritative source. However, if you are using the phone book, you must use a recent one. If you look in a book dated 1940, you may not find your friend listed at all, or you may find an old number that is no longer correct.

Perhaps you want to know the best way to get to the Grand Canyon. Again you refer to an authority. Either you look up the route on a road map of the United States, or you discuss it with an expert on travel. However, if you are planning to go by automobile, reference to an airline's map won't help you very much, because it is an authority on a different form of travel.

Reference to authority is one of the simplest ways of gaining information, but a decided danger is associated with this method. Authorities are not always correct, as the following examples show.

1. Aristotle (384–322 B.C.) was an outstanding Greek scientist. His studies had a tremendous effect on world knowledge, and his books became the final authority on almost everything. But, although Aristotle was a great scientist, many of his ideas were completely wrong. For example, he believed that most diseases were spread by a miasm or cloud of infected air which surrounds the person suffering from the disease. According to Aristotle, when conditions were right, this cloud could spread and cause an epidemic. Because this idea was favored by Aristotle, a truly great authority, it had a profound effect on doctors for many hundreds of years, even though it was wrong.

2. The work of Galen was considered to be the last word on human anatomy for a period of about 1200 years. Galen was the authority. He could not be wrong. Unfortunately, when Galen lived (A.D. 130–200) dissection of the human body was forbidden. Galen drew his conclusions about human anatomy from dissections of apes and other animals. Even though Galen was an outstanding scientist, with wonderful powers of observation, it is obvious that much of what he said about the human body was wrong. Yet, his words were accepted as truth for many centuries after his death. It was only when Andreas Vesalius (1514–1564) and others carried out actual dissections of human bodies that many of these errors were corrected.

3. It sometimes happens that authorities are so certain of themselves that they make dogmatic statements which come back to haunt them later on. Take, for example, the case of the famous nineteenth-century chemist who undertook the project of analyzing foods, and establishing the perfect diet. He broke down foods into carbohydrates, fats, proteins, minerals, and water, and he carefully measured the proportions. After these exhaustive studies, he concluded that there was nothing further to learn about the science of nutrition. Everything important was already known. A few short years later, vitamins were discovered, and the whole field of nutrition was blown wide open.

A similar incident involved a Nobel Prize winner in physics, who was reported to have said in 1894 that the science of physics was so well established, there was practically nothing left to discover. The very next year, in 1895, William Roentgen discovered X rays, and thus opened the door for the new field of radiation physics.

4. Perhaps the most famous example of mistaken attitudes on the part of respected authorities concerns the story of Edward Jenner and the report he tried to make before the Royal Society on his work with vaccination against smallpox. When Jenner was a student of medicine in Sodbury, England, he asked a young girl about smallpox and she replied, " I cannot take that disease, for I have had cowpox." This idea, that people who had contracted cowpox from cattle became immune to smallpox, was accepted by many of the farmers and milkmaids of the region, but was laughed at by the doctors. However, the idea intrigued Jenner, and he continued to keep it in mind when he began practice as a country doctor. He confided to a friend, under a promise of strict secrecy, that some day he was going to try vaccination against smallpox.

In 1796 Jenner made his first successful vaccination. He transferred material from a cowpox sore on the hand of a milkmaid named Sarah Nelmes to an eight-year-old boy named James Phipps. During the next two years he continued to experiment, and he made many other successful vaccinations. Then he thought the time was ripe to publicize his discovery. In 1798 he applied to the Royal Society for permission to present his discovery before this group of great scientists. Here was the greatest group of authorities of that day on science, and *they refused to grant Jenner permission even to present his report.* They advised him that he ought not to risk his reputation by presenting to the learned body " anything which seemed so at variance with established knowledge, and withal so incredible "!

Naturally Jenner was disappointed and discouraged, but he published his results anyway. The idea of vaccination proved itself to such an extent that in 1802, only four years later, the English Parliament voted him a grant of twenty thousand pounds (nearly $100,000) for making this amazing discovery. Other honors and awards were soon heaped on Jenner from all parts of the world.

The authorities, who could not accept an idea " so at variance with established knowledge," turned out to be dead wrong. And Jenner's " incredible " idea became one of the greatest medical discoveries of all time.

The story of Edward Jenner illustrates the serious danger that authoritative sources tend to become the final word on a subject. They sometimes become inflexible and rigid, even to the extent of *opposing* new discoveries. Keep in mind, therefore, that authorities are to be respected — but they are not always right.

5 Observation

One of the most important methods of obtaining information is by observation. The word *observe* means "to see," but observation includes more than seeing. It includes the use of all the senses and all the scientific instruments to learn what is occurring. Thus, a blind man can observe, even though he cannot see. Observations can be made by seeing, hearing, tasting, smelling, feeling, counting, weighing, measuring, and by many other methods.

For example, you walk into a dark room where you cannot see a thing. Almost immediately you say, "The gas jet is open." How did you know? You made an observation — you *smelled* gas.

Or the cook wants to know if he has properly seasoned the soup. He makes a simple observation. He *tastes* the soup.

Or you are sandpapering a piece of furniture in preparation for a fine lacquer finish. You run your fingers over the wood to *feel* whether it is smooth enough.

Or you want to know how much carpeting to buy for your living room. You get a yardstick and *measure* the room. Then, by applying simple arithmetic, you determine how many square yards of carpet you will need.

Or you come upon a man lying unconscious on the ground. You want to know if he is alive. You put your ear to his chest and *listen*. You *hear* the heart beat, and you conclude that he is still alive.

As you see, observation is a commonplace act which is part of everyday living. It is also one of the most important ways by which a scientist obtains information. However, scientists do not depend entirely upon their own senses. Sometimes the human senses are not acute enough to make the necessary observations, and frequently they are misleading.

You can easily convince yourself that your senses are not always to be depended on by carrying out a simple test like this. Put your right hand into a pot of ice water, and your left hand into a pot of water at about 150°F. Keep them in their respective pots for a few minutes, and then put both hands into a pot of water at about 75°F. The water will feel warm to your right hand, and cold to your left hand. Which hand is telling you the truth?

It is common knowledge that our eyes frequently deceive us. Consider, for example, the five lines shown in Figure 5. Two of them are exactly equal in length. Look at them carefully, and see if you can choose the two equal lines. Now take a ruler and measure them. Did your eyes tell you the truth?

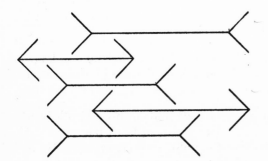

FIGURE **5.**
Sometimes our senses cannot be depended upon for accurate observation. Which two of these lines are equal in length?

Because scientists cannot always trust their senses, they have devised instruments which make the senses more acute or more accurate. Thus, the microscope, the telescope, and the X-ray machine enable the scientist to see things which he couldn't possibly see with the unaided eye. The micrometer, the voltmeter, and the analytic balance are among the thousands of instruments which give accuracy to the observations of the scientist. Yet the most important "instrument" of all is the scientist's brain, which he uses for *plain, hard thinking.* Let us consider a few cases in which instruments are used or have been used to make observations.

1. Your portable radio stops working. The radio man tests the battery with a voltmeter and says, "You need a new battery. This one is dead." With the help of the voltmeter, he has observed that the battery does not supply sufficient voltage to operate your set.

2. The detective investigating a shooting wants to know if the bullet came from a certain gun. He fires another bullet from the gun, and then by using a comparison microscope, he observes whether or not the markings on the two bullets match.

3. The discovery of protozoa, bacteria, and other microorganisms was dependent upon the use of an early microscope. By grinding lenses and using them to extend the ability of his eyes to see, Leeuwenhoek discovered and described many kinds of " animalcules " which were invisible to the naked eye.

4. Suppose you want to know if a certain piece of food contains starch. You carry out a simple test. You add iodine to a sample of the food, and you observe the color which results. A purple or black color indicates the presence of starch. In this case, you have extended your senses by means of a chemical reaction which causes a color change if starch is present. You have used another scientific " instrument " — chemical reaction.

5. It is interesting to note that even before helium was known to exist on the earth, it was discovered on the sun by observations made with the spectroscope.

6. A doctor wants to get information about his patient's heart. He takes the pulse, and *counts* the number of beats per minute. At the same time he *feels* whether the pulse is strong or weak. He *listens* to the heart with a stethoscope. He records the action on an electrocardiogram so that he has a *visual* record of the action of the heart. All of these are methods of observing the heart.

7. Consider the case of John Snow. His observations demonstrated the way in which cholera spreads. This was done in 1854, twenty-nine years before Robert Koch discovered the comma-shaped bacterium which causes the disease. During a terrible epidemic of cholera in London, Snow plotted every case on a map of the city. In this instance his scientific " instrument " was a combination of his brain and a map. As case after case was added to the map, a pattern began to appear. It seemed to center about a certain water pump. Now Dr. Snow became a detective. He tracked down each case, and showed that every one of the affected people had used water from this very pump. His accurate observations led to the inference that infected water causes the spread of cholera.

It is fairly safe to say that observation plays a great part in all scientific work. In fact, some branches of science depend almost entirely upon observation. For example, the science of astronomy must by its very nature depend almost exclusively upon observation. Similarly, the study of comparative anatomy is almost purely observation, consisting of learning the details of structure of various animals and comparing similar structures in different animals. But regardless of whether a science depends entirely or only partly on observation, one thing is certain. It must be accurate observation, and it must be complete observation. It is not enough to observe one facet and forget about the others. One-sided observation may lead to an incorrect solution of the problem at hand.

Consider the famous case of "The Blind Men and the Elephant," so ably described in a poem by John Godfrey Saxe (1816–1887). As the story goes, six wise men of India were going to discover what an elephant is like. Unfortunately, each of the six men was blind. Each man approached the elephant in turn, and — but let the poem tell the story in its own way.

> It was six men of Indostan
> To learning much inclined,
> Who went to see the Elephant
> (Though all of them were blind),
> That each by observation
> Might satisfy his mind.

> The *First* approached the Elephant,
> And happening to fall
> Against his broad and sturdy side,
> At once began to bawl:
> " God bless me! but the Elephant
> Is very like a wall! "

> The *Second*, feeling of the tusk,
> Cried, " Ho! what have we here
> So very round and smooth and sharp?
> To me 'tis mighty clear
> This wonder of an Elephant
> Is very like a spear! "

> The *Third* approached the animal,
> And happening to take
> The squirming trunk within his hands,
> Thus boldly up and spake:
> " I see," quoth he, " the Elephant
> Is very like a snake! "

> The *Fourth* reached out an eager hand,
> And felt about the knee.
> " What most this wondrous beast is like
> Is mighty plain," quoth he;
> " 'Tis clear enough the Elephant
> Is very like a tree! "

The *Fifth* who chanced to touch the ear,
Said: " E'n the blindest man
Can tell what this resembles most;
Deny the fact who can,
This marvel of an Elephant
Is very like a fan! "

The *Sixth* no sooner had begun
About the beast to grope,
Than, seizing on the swinging tail
That fell within his scope,
" I see," quoth he, " the Elephant
Is very like a rope! "

Each of the blind men did in fact make an accurate observation, within the limits of his ability (Figure 6). Yet each of them was definitely wrong in his description of the elephant, because the observation was quite incomplete. In the words of the poem:

And so these men of Indostan
Disputed loud and long,
Each in his own opinion
Exceeding stiff and strong,
Though each was partly in the right,
And all were in the wrong!

FIGURE **6.** *If scientific observations are to be accurate, they must be complete. What mistaken impressions have these six blind men formed about an elephant?*

6 Trial and Error

Trial and error seems like a very unscientific way of obtaining information, yet much can be accomplished in this way. In order to clarify the meaning of trial and error, let us consider the actions of an animal in a maze.

If a hungry rat is put into a maze, he begins to explore. He sniffs this way and that, he goes back and forth, he enters nearly every passage and covers nearly every inch of the maze. He runs into an alley, and when it turns out to be a blind alley, he turns back and tries another. After repeatedly wandering around blindly, exploring and sniffing, the animal accidentally finds his way to the food box which lies at the end of the correct path.

If the rat is now returned to the beginning of the maze, he repeats his aimless wanderings, but perhaps with a little more speed and less waste of time in some of the blind alleys. On the trials which follow, he does not go as deep into the blind alleys, and eventually he passes the openings to the blind alleys without even turning his head. Instead, he runs along the correct path directly to the food. He has learned by repeated trials which paths lead to blind alleys and which lead to the food. He has tried them all, and he has learned to eliminate the wrong paths, or errors.

Much human learning is also the result of trial and error; and many scientific discoveries have been made in the same way. Here are some examples of how trial and error can be applied.

1. Suppose someone gives you a puzzle which consists of two interlocking keys. You are supposed to take them apart. You begin by twisting and turning the keys every which way until suddenly they come apart. If you repeat the process several times, you gradually eliminate your errors, and learn to take the keys apart promptly and effortlessly.

2. Perhaps you are a fisherman out for bass. You are using minnows for bait without success. So you switch to worms. The bass aren't taking worms, so you try grasshoppers or frogs. Finally you use dobsons, and bang! You get a strike! By trial and error you have determined which of your five or six kinds of bait the bass are taking today.

3. Suppose you have a dozen different stains, and you want to find out which one will best bring out certain structures of a tissue which is to be studied under the microscope. There is only one thing to do. You must try them one after the other until you find the one which does the most effective job.

4. Perhaps you are learning to drive a car, and you are practicing parallel parking between two other cars at the curb. When you first begin, you may turn the wheel the wrong way, or you may cut it too sharply or not sharply enough. After making several errors, you begin to eliminate the incorrect acts. After a great many trials, you learn to park well enough to pass your driving test.

5. Consider the statement made by Paul Müller, winner of the Nobel Prize in 1948 for his discovery of the value of DDT as an insecticide. In his lecture he said, " After fruitless testing of hundreds of different substances, I realized that it is not easy to find a good contact insecticide." He had been testing hundreds of substances, one after the other, until he tried dichloro-diphenyl-trichloroethane (DDT for short). Then his trial-and-error procedure was rewarded, and a new scientific discovery was made.

6. Another example is the case of Paul Ehrlich, who was interested in finding a specific drug for syphilis which would be more harmful to the germ of the disease than to human beings. He was looking for what some people call " a magic bullet " which would kill the parasite without injuring the host. Ehrlich knew that arsenic compounds killed the germ, but they would also kill the human patient. So, he began the thankless task of taking a toxic arsenic compound, and modifying its chemical structure in different ways, in the hope of finding one modification which suited his requirements. He did this 605 times without success. Each modified compound was a failure. However, compound 606 was successful, and the substance known as arsphenamine or Salvarsan was added to the list of useful drugs in the hands of physicians. From 1909, when it was discovered, to about 1943 Salvarsan was the drug of choice in the treatment of syphilis. Since 1943 penicillin and other antibiotics have replaced it. Nonetheless, Salvarsan was an important drug discovered by a trial-and-error procedure.

7. The finding of new antibiotic substances also illustrates how trial-and-error methods may uncover useful substances. Dr. Selman A. Waksman and his co-workers discovered several new antibiotics by taking fungi from the soil at random and testing these fungi for their effect against bacteria. Dr. Waksman tested hundreds of different soil organisms, and eliminated all those which showed no effect. Using this trial-and-error method, he and his associates discovered streptomycin in 1944. Streptomycin gave medicine a new weapon in its battle against many diseases, especially tuberculosis. In 1952 Dr. Waksman was awarded a Nobel Prize for his work.

8. The bark of the quinaquina tree was a remedy for malaria long used by the Indians of Peru. Legend has it that in 1638 it was used to save the life of the malaria-stricken Countess of Chinchon, wife of the Spanish governor of Peru. Two years later, when she was returning to Spain, she supposedly took some of the bark with her. Although she died on the way, it was claimed that the bark got to Spain, thus introducing Europe to the treatment of malaria with what was called Peruvian bark, or cinchona bark (after the Countess).* However, not all samples of cinchona bark were equally effective, and the question arose as to what substance in the bark was responsible for its curative power. If the effective substance could be extracted and purified, the variable value of different barks could be overcome. Many chemists and pharmacists all over the world began to take the bark apart in an effort to find the effective substance. They extracted many different substances, and there followed a trial-and-error testing procedure. But each trial was a failure; each extracted substance failed to cure malaria. Finally, in 1820, two French pharmacists, Pierre J. Pelletier and Joseph B. Caventou, extracted a substance which they named quinine after the old Indian name for the tree. After all previous trials had failed, this one was successful in getting the essential ingredient of cinchona bark.

9. In 1775 Dr. William Withering in England introduced the herb foxglove (digitalis) for the treatment of dropsy. In describing

---

* The truth of this legend is disputed by many authorities. Nonetheless, by some means the bark was introduced to Europe.

his discovery, Dr. Withering wrote: " In the year 1775 my opinion was asked concerning a family receipt [recipe] for the cure of the dropsy. I was told that it had long been kept a secret by an old woman in Shropshire, who had sometimes made cures after the more regular practitioners had failed. . . . This medicine was composed of twenty or more different herbs." Dr. Withering eliminated the herbs one at a time, and finally discovered that the active herb was foxglove. In his practice he used water extracts of the foxglove. But he got variable reactions to the drug from different patients. In some cases a small dose was effective, while in other cases it had no effect at all. So Dr. Withering worked out a trial-and-error procedure for determining the correct dose for each individual patient. He began with a small dose, and gradually increased the dose until he got the desired effect.

10. In the fight against different forms of cancer, many drugs are tested. In 1946, a scientist working under an American Cancer Society research fellowship tested about one hundred different compounds belonging to the nitrogen mustard family to see if he could find one which might be promising. He found four out of the hundred tested which he thought might be useful. These were tested on people suffering from leukemia. Unfortunately, even these four compounds were found " to have little or nothing to offer in cases of acute leukemia." But the scientist did not give up. During 1948–1950 he tested 250 compounds of a different kind on mice suffering from leukemia. He still found only four that showed promise. Again these compounds, tested on people, did not cure the condition although they did give temporary relief. At the present time this particular problem has not been solved; but trial-and-error testing of drugs continues. Perhaps eventually some researcher will find *the drug* which will cure leukemia.

These and other examples show that trial and error, although it seems to be an unscientific way of doing something, is still the method best suited to solve certain kinds of everyday problems and certain kinds of science problems.

7 Experiment

In the mind of the average person, the word *scientist* is always associated with the word *experiment* (or *planned experiment*). Yet the preceding pages have tried to show that scientists do not always perform experiments. Many famous discoveries have been made without a single experiment. As a matter of fact, it is almost impossible to perform experiments in certain fields of science such as astronomy, comparative anatomy, anthropology (the study of man and his cultures), and paleontology (the study of fossils). Still, it is no more than right that experiments and scientists should be thought of together, since of all the weapons in the armory of science, the planned experiment has proved to be one of the most effective. It has been said that modern science *began* with the introduction of the planned experiment into the search for knowledge.

Actually, the planned experiment is nothing more than the process of making something happen under conditions controlled by the observer. It is a situation planned and set up by the experimenter, which will give him the answer to a certain specific question, because all other conditions or possibilities have been eliminated. It does not have to be a complicated affair. Some of the outstanding experiments in science have been startling by virtue of their very simplicity (for instance, Redi's experiment on spontaneous generation described in Chapter 3). However, all planned experiments do have certain basic things in common. Perhaps we can best discuss these basic characteristics by taking a simple question, planning an experiment to answer it, and analyzing the experiment which has been set up. For example, to answer the question "Do Seeds Need Water in Order to Sprout into Plants?" we might set up the following experiment. We can plant a seed in some dry soil within a bottle and let the bottle of soil stand unwatered for several days. We observe that the seed does not sprout. Can we conclude from this that seeds will sprout only if they are watered?

A moment's reflection will show that such a conclusion is not valid. All we know is that the seed did not sprout. From the experiment as it was performed *we cannot tell exactly why the seed failed to sprout.* Here are a few possible reasons:

1. Perhaps the seed did not sprout because it lacked water.
2. Perhaps the seed itself was dead.
3. Perhaps the soil was poor.
4. Perhaps a bottle is not a suitable place in which to have seeds sprout.
5. Maybe it was too hot or too cold.
6. Maybe the light was too strong or too weak.

We have, above, a whole string of possible explanations as to why the seed failed to sprout. Yet we cannot tell which one is the correct explanation because *our experiment was poorly designed.* It violated several of the rules which all good experiments must follow. Let us see how we can improve our experiment.

The question is still the same: " Do Seeds Need Water in Order to Sprout into Plants? " Our experiment, however, is somewhat modified. This time we use *two similar bottles* instead of one. We get some dry soil and divide it into two equal portions — one for each bottle. We plant a seed of the same variety in each bottle. Lastly, *we water the soil in bottle No. 1, but we do not water the soil in bottle No. 2* (Figure 7), and we keep both bottles in the same place.

FIGURE **7.** *To find out whether seeds need water in order to sprout, you need to set up an experiment in two parts, as shown here. Why are both parts of the experiment necessary?*

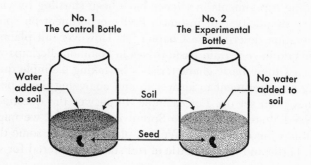

No. 1
The Control Bottle

No. 2
The Experimental Bottle

Water added to soil

No water added to soil

Soil

Seed

We observe that the seed in bottle No. 1 did sprout, but that the seed in bottle No. 2 did not sprout. So we ask ourselves why this happened.

1. Was it because bottle No. 1 is a better place for plant growth than bottle No. 2?	1. No, because both bottles were exactly the same, even to the soil that was used in them.
2. Was it because the light or heat conditions were better in one bottle than in the other?	2. No, because both bottles were kept in the same place.
3. Was it because the seed in bottle No. 1 got water while the seed in bottle No. 2 did not?	3. *Possibly this is the correct answer.*
4. Was it because the seed in bottle No. 1 was alive while the seed in bottle No. 2 was dead?	4. *Possibly this is the correct answer.*

Apparently this setup is better than the first, since it enables us to eliminate some of the possible explanations as to why the seed did or did not grow. What was there about this setup which made it better than the first? Why were we able to eliminate the bottle, the soil, the temperature, the light, as factors preventing the sprouting of the seed? Simply because in another identical bottle with the same soil under the same conditions, a seed did sprout!

Then this experiment is better than the first because *it has two parts* which we can compare. Still, we cannot reach a valid answer to our question. We are left with at least two possible answers. Perhaps the seed in bottle No. 2 did not grow because it received no water. Or possibly it did not grow because it was dead. Evidently we must plan our experiment so that it gives us only one possible answer to our question. We cannot afford to allow for two possible answers, because, if we do, we will never know which is the correct answer to our question.

Another modification of the experiment is necessary to make sure we get only one possible answer. It seems reasonable that if we design our experiment so that there is *only one difference between the two parts,* then only one answer is possible — whatever single answer is caused by the single difference.

Thus, we have learned so far that a well-planned experiment must have *two parts with a single experimental difference between them.* One of these parts is known as the experimental part of the experiment, and the other is called the control or check part. For example, in the setup just described, we were trying to get seeds to sprout without benefit of water. The bottle which was watered might be considered the control part, while the unwatered bottle might be called the experimental part.

Still, this experiment is not good enough. It does not answer our question because more than one difference exists between the two parts. So, what can we do to improve the experiment still further? Obviously we must eliminate the danger of dead seeds. Suppose we repeat the same experiment over and over again, always getting the same result. Or suppose we plant several seeds from the same packet in each bottle instead of just a single seed. It is highly improbable that all the seeds planted in bottle No. 1 are alive while all those planted in bottle No. 2 are dead. Now then, if the seeds in bottle No. 1 always sprout, while those in bottle No. 2 never sprout, it must be due to the presence of water in bottle No. 1 and the absense of water in bottle No. 2. This leads us to the next requirement of a good experiment. Not only must there be two parts with a single difference, but *there must be a large number of cases in both the experimental and control groups.*

After repeating the experiment with many seeds, we are ready to conclude at last that seeds need water to sprout into plants. But wait! Can we really form this conclusion? We have tested only one kind of seed. Is the same true of other kinds of seeds? Again we do not know. So we must modify our conclusion to " seeds of the kind we tested need water to sprout," until other kinds of seeds have been tested.

To summarize — in planning a well-designed experiment, the following rules must be considered:

1. The experiment must have two parts for comparison:
   a. the experimental or variable part testing a condition.
   b. the check or control part which is kept constant.
2. There must be only one variable — only one difference — between the experimental group and the control group. Thus, there will be but one question to be answered.
3. There must be a large number of cases in both the experimental group and the control group.

4. The experiment must be such that it can be repeated by any other person who wants to do so, and who has the necessary skills.

5. The conclusion must not be expected to include a wider area than the experimental materials allow.

Now that we understand the basic requirements of a good experiment, let us consider a few examples which illustrate how these requirements are satisfied. Suppose you wanted to know whether seeds need light to sprout into plants. You could set up several flowerpots of the same size, each containing the same kind of soil. Divide the flowerpots into pairs, marked:

No. 1 light, No. 1 dark
No. 2 light, No. 2 dark
No. 3 light, No. 3 dark

In each pot of pair No. 1, plant several bean seeds.
In each pot of pair No. 2, plant several corn seeds.
In each pot of pair No. 3, plant several marigold seeds.

Now water all the pots, and place them all in a spot where they are exposed to light, but cover all the " dark " pots with a light-proof container so that no light reaches them. Leave them this way, but water them regularly. After the necessary time has elapsed, you will observe that the seeds have sprouted in all the pots, those in the light and those in the dark equally well. From this observation, you can conclude that seeds do not need light in order to sprout into plants.

Notice that this experiment did give a single answer to the question in the problem. We were able to reach a single answer for these reasons:

1. The experiment had two parts: an experimental part consisting of several pots of seeds kept in the dark; and a control part consisting of an equal number of pots kept in the light.

2. There was only a single difference between the control part and the experimental part. The pots were the same; the soil was the same; the water was the same; the seeds were the same; and all other conditions were the same *except for one* — light as opposed to darkness.

3. The experiment included many cases. That is to say, there were several seeds of a given variety in the control pot, and an equal number of seeds of the same variety in the experimental pot.

4. Several varieties of seeds were tested rather than one, so that a general conclusion could be reached.

5. This experiment was designed so that it can be repeated by anyone who wishes to do so, with the same results.

Of course, the experiment we just considered is a comparatively simple one. Suppose we now turn our attention to a somewhat more complicated case. Let us assume that you want to perform an experiment to find the effect of the minerals sodium, potassium, iodine, iron, and copper on the growth of rats. To set up this experiment properly, you will need six groups of rats — one control group and five experimental groups, one for each mineral. You must make your groups as equal as possible in every way, such as size, weight, age, sex, health, and heredity. One way of controlling these factors is to use litter-mates of a purebred strain of rats. By litter-mates we mean babies born at the same time to one pair of parents. Naturally, if the parents are purebred the children will be as close together in heredity as you can hope to get. The only thing closer would be identical twins.

Suppose that you can get six litters of baby rats, each litter consisting of six male animals of almost identical characteristics. You now separate each litter so that rat No. 1 goes into the control cage, rat No. 2 into the "no sodium" cage, rat No. 3 into the "no potassium" cage, rat No. 4 into the "no iodine" cage, rat No. 5 into the "no iron" cage, and rat No. 6 into the "no copper" cage. Thus, each cage ends up with six rats, one from each of the six litters.

Notice that there is only one control cage for five experimental cages. This is quite proper, since it would be wasteful of materials, time, and money to set up six different controls which are actually the same. The single control group can be used for comparison with each experimental group in turn.

Once you have your six groups set up, you are ready to go ahead with the feeding. All the groups receive a diet of purified nutrients consisting of essential amino acids, glucose, fats, and vitamins. This basic part of the diet is identical for all the groups, but you add a different mineral salt mixture to the diet of each group. Thus, the control group gets a salt mixture containing all the mineral salts which we believe to be necessary for good health. To the diet of the "no sodium" group we add a similar salt mixture, but one which contains no sodium. The "no potassium" group gets a salt mixture containing no potassium, and so on for the other groups.

We give all the animals the same care. We give them all the water they want, and keep the cages clean. We observe them regularly, weigh them, measure them, watch them carefully, and keep accurate records of their growth, their activities, and their development. After this continues for some time, we may begin to observe noticeable differences as we *compare each group in turn with the control group.* Ultimately, we may be able to reach a conclusion concerning the lack of these minerals in the diet of rats.

However, we must be cautious not to generalize with respect to other animals because of what we observe in our experiments on rats. It does not necessarily follow that because rats react in a particular way to certain dietary conditions, mice or dogs or humans will show similar reactions. It is possible that they might, but that would have to be discovered by another planned experiment. To illustrate by an actual example:

In the early days of research in the vitamins, a disagreement arose among scientists as to the importance of Vitamin C. Some scientists said that in their experiments the animals fed a diet lacking in Vitamin C became ill with scurvy and died. Other scientists doing exactly the same experiment, and using exactly the same diets, found that their animals stayed healthy. The trouble was that the two groups of scientists were using different animals in their experiments. Those who used rats found that the lack of Vitamin C had no effect, while those who were using guinea pigs found that the animals became ill. We know today that rats have inherited the ability to manufacture Vitamin C from certain other things in their diet. However, guinea pigs (and men, too) cannot manufacture their own Vitamin C, and so they must get it in their diet or become ill.

Now that we have considered several theoretical experiments, let us examine two actual ones which were performed by scientists. Let us start by re-examining one of Redi's experiments. This experiment has already been described in Chapter 3 to illustrate the methods of science. It will be worthwhile to consider it once again at this point, because this experiment is a model of care and simplicity. In the report of his carefully planned experiment, Redi says:

. . . I began to believe that all worms found in meat were derived directly from the droppings of flies, and not from the putrefaction of the meat. . . . Belief would be useless without the confirmation of an experiment. Therefore in the middle of July I put a snake, some fish, some eels . . . and a slice of milk-fed veal in four large wide-mouthed flasks; and sealed them well. I then filled four more flasks in the same way, only leaving these open. It was not long before the meat and fish in the open vessels became wormy, and flies were seen entering and leaving at will. But in the closed flasks, I did not see a worm. . . . Not content with these experiments, I tried many others at different seasons, using different vessels . . .

What makes this a good experiment? In answer to this question, we can list the following points:

1. It had two parts — an experimental part with several closed flasks and a control part with an equal number of open flasks.

2. There was only one difference between the two parts. Every flask in the experimental part was kept tightly closed so that flies could not get in, while every flask in the control part was kept open so that flies could enter freely.

3. There were many cases in the experiment. Redi tried the experiment repeatedly at different seasons and with different vessels.

4. Several varieties of meat and fish were tested, so that a general conclusion could be reached.

5. The experiment was so designed that it can be repeated time and time again with the same results, if the same care is taken.

For all these reasons, Redi's simple, clear-cut experiment gave him the answer to the question. It showed quite plainly that maggots are not generated spontaneously in decaying meat.

The history of medicine includes many reports of classic experiments. Frequently a vaccine or a treatment must be tested experimentally. To do it properly requires a tremendous number of subjects and careful statistical analysis of the results. It also requires something else — control of the psychological factors involved. People may react to an injection merely because it is an injection, and not because of the material which is injected. Therefore, the scientist must devise ways to cancel out psychological reactions in both the experimental group and the control group. One way of doing this is by using a *placebo*, an inert substance which has no effect. The experimental group is injected with the vaccine, and the control group is injected with the placebo. This is done under such conditions that the subjects do not know whether they are getting the real vaccine or the inert substance.

The fight against polio has taken a tremendous forward step as the result of a mass experiment performed in 1954. Working un-

FIGURE **8.** *The polio vaccine experiment was one of the largest scale experiments ever planned and carried out. Over 1,800,000 school children took part. The experimental group received injections of vaccine, while the control groups received dummy shots or no injections at all. The question was, " Does the vaccine help prevent polio?" The answer — yes!*

der a grant from the National Foundation for Infantile Paralysis, Dr. Jonas Salk had devised a vaccine which seemed to show great promise toward inducing immunity to polio. The vaccine was prepared by growing three different strains of polio viruses on slivers of monkey kidney in test tubes. After a certain period of incubation and growth, the viruses were killed by chemical means, and the vaccine was purified. The chemical treatment made the viruses incapable of causing disease, but when injected into the blood stream, they could still cause antibodies against polio to be produced.

After testing the vaccine on animals, and finding it safe and effective, Dr. Salk went ahead to try it on humans. Included in the preliminary tests were Dr. Salk's own three children. When these tests satisfied Dr. Salk and his sponsors that the vaccine was effective, a large-scale experiment was planned to evaluate the vaccine thoroughly.

The experiment was planned on a tremendous scale so as to include children from every part of the United States, particularly from those areas where there is a great deal of polio. Three injections of vaccine were given to 440,000 school children, while a control group of another 210,000 youngsters received placebo, or "dummy" shots. In addition, approximately 1,180,000 children who received no injections at all participated in the study as a second control group. In all, a total of 1,830,000 school children were involved in the experiment. To make the conditions as similar as possible for the experimental and control groups, every bottle of injection material looked exactly alike, so that not even the doctor who did the injecting could tell whether he was using the real vaccine or the placebo. The only identification was provided by a code number on each bottle, and the code number was meaningful only to those scientists who planned the experiment.

The injections were made (Figure 8). A period of waiting began. Every injected child was watched as the polio season came along, and an accurate record for each child was kept in a central office. The record included information on age, sex, the area in which the child lived, the kind of health and educational facilities available, and other data. All of these factors would be important in analyzing the results of the test, and many statisticians were kept busy recording and analyzing.

Unfortunately, some of the children in the experiment did develop polio, but the percentage of polio victims among those who got the Salk vaccine was far smaller than among those who got the placebo or received no injection at all. Because of this, it was concluded that the Salk vaccine did effectively protect against polio, and a full-scale program was begun in 1955 to give the vaccine to every child whose parents advocated the vaccination.

Although this experiment sounds quite simple, it was complicated by the extensive statistical records required. Planning such a complex operation is not the work of one man. It requires the combined brains of many outstanding men to develop the plan and carry it out. If you will analyze the Salk vaccine experiment, you will find that it satisfies each of the conditions of a good experiment.

8 Serendipity — The Art of Being Lucky

Many discoveries in science are made as a result of chance incidents. While it may or may not be true that Sir Isaac Newton discovered the law of gravity because an apple fell on his head, it is a definite fact that a scientist working on some problem may discover something important which is altogether unrelated to the problem at hand. Chance discovery is known as *serendipity* — the art of finding something you are not seeking. Yet it depends upon more than chance, for it implies that you must be able to recognize a chance discovery and realize its importance.

The word serendipity was originated by Horace Walpole over two hundred years ago, based on the old fairy tale about *The Three Princes of Serendip.* " As their highnesses traveled, they were always making discoveries, by accidents and by sagacity, of things they were not in quest of." Walpole coined the word to use as a bit of conversational nonsense.

Although the word serendipity was originated in a fairy tale, scientists know that it is no fairy tale in the laboratory. The art of being lucky is as real as research work. However, research workers know that being lucky is one thing, whereas *being observant enough to realize that you have been lucky* is quite another thing. The important part of serendipity is being able to realize that an unexpected event may be the beginning of something important, as the following examples show:

1. William Herschel, the famous English astronomer, is usually credited with the discovery in 1781 of the planet Uranus. Actually, he was not looking for a new planet at all. He was studying a certain sector of the sky when he observed an object which seemed to be too large for a star. He became interested, and studied this object. To his surprise, he discovered that it was moving among

the stars, and he concluded that this must be a new planet, which was previously unknown. Later, records were found showing that this "star" had been observed and recorded at least twenty times during the hundred years preceding Herschel's discovery. In each case, it was set down simply as a star, and the observer did not think it worthy of further study. Herschel was the first man to recognize that he had discovered something different, and to him goes the credit for the discovery of the planet Uranus.

2. Take the case of Alexander Fleming. He was not the first bacteriologist to observe that when molds contaminate bacterial cultures, the bacteria may not grow very well. But all the others were simply annoyed by the fact that their cultures were contaminated. Only Fleming thought it worthwhile to investigate, even though it had nothing to do with the problem he was studying. As a result, in 1945 he shared a Nobel Prize with H. W. Florey and E. B. Chain "for the discovery of penicillin and its therapeutic effect for the cure of different infectious maladies."

True, it was only by chance that a mold got into one of Fleming's dishes of staphylococci, but it was something more than chance which enabled him to turn this trivial event into a great discovery. It was a remarkable alertness for the unexpected, a "rare ability to profit by nature's slightest deviation . . . that explains why some men turn to most remarkably good advantage seemingly trivial accidents." [*] As Pasteur once put it, "Chance favors the prepared mind."

Yes, fortune favors the experimenter who is prepared to take notice of chance results. But don't confuse "chance" with "luck." "Luck" implies some mystical element, some control by the supernatural; whereas "chance" refers simply to an event which occurs normally, even though it is not planned for or anticipated. There is nothing mystical or supernatural about the chance discoveries of scientists.

3. Consider the good fortune of William H. Perkin. In 1856 this young man, at the ripe age of eighteen, came home from school on vacation and decided that he was going to find a way to make quinine synthetically out of coal tar products. In 1850 the French Society of Pharmacy had offered a prize of four thousand francs for the chemist who could discover a way of preparing quinine artificially. This prize had not yet been claimed.

[*] Alan Gregg, *The Furtherance of Medical Research*, Yale University Press.

Perkin set up a laboratory in the attic of his house and went to work. He tried many different combinations of compounds, but each time he got only a black sticky mass in the bottom of the test tubes. After one series of experiments, while trying to clean up the mess in his test tubes with alcohol, he noticed a beautiful purple color of delicate hue. It occurred to him that this might make a good dye. It did! The color was named aniline purple or *mauve*, and soon it became so popular that the period is sometimes referred to as the " mauve decade."

No, Perkin did not win the four thousand francs offered for synthetic quinine, but he did discover the first important artificial dye in history. This discovery in 1856 laid the basis for the whole coal tar industry, and showed other chemists the way to synthesize many other organic substances.

4. Just as unexpected was the discovery of X rays by William C. Roentgen in 1895. He was experimenting with electrical discharges in vacuum tubes of the type known as Crookes tubes. While working in a dark room, he observed that a special fluorescent screen began to glow, even though it was about six or seven feet away from the Crookes tube with which he was working, and even though the Crookes tube was entirely covered with black paper. Now, of course, everybody knew that light could not pass through black paper. So it was with great surprise that Roentgen realized that he had discovered something new — rays that could penetrate black paper. More surprising still, these mysterious rays could pass through sheets of metal. Rays with such mysterious powers well deserved the name X rays which Roentgen bestowed upon them. He had never dreamed of such rays when he began his observations on vacuum tubes. For that matter, no one else believed such rays were possible. When the news of Roentgen's X rays got into the papers, he was bitterly attacked by people who refused to believe that invisible rays could pass through opaque substances. He was called a charlatan, a faker. Yet, shortly after the discovery, X rays were used by a doctor in the United States to locate a bullet imbedded in a wound. Roentgen was awarded the Nobel Prize in Physics in 1901.

5. Another Nobel Prize winner also attributes his discovery to an unexpected occurrence. In 1913 Charles Richet was awarded the Nobel Prize " in recognition of his work on anaphylaxis." He had been experimenting with the poisons which are injected by the tentacles of certain sea animals such as the " Portuguese Man of War " and the sea anemones. He extracted the poison and injected it into dogs. Many of the dogs died, but a few survived and seemed to recover completely after two or three weeks.

Now Richet started a new experiment. He injected the recovered dogs once again. He expected one of two possible results:

a. If the dogs had really recovered with no change, then giving them a second dose of the poison should make them sick again with the same symptoms they showed after the first injection.

b. If, on the other hand, the original injection had brought about some change in the dogs, they should now be less sensitive to the poison, or even totally immune. In this case, the injection of a second dose of toxin should have less effect than the original dose.

Imagine his surprise when he found that injecting a tiny dose of the toxin into dogs which had recovered from an earlier full dose caused very severe reactions and rapid death. The dogs were now apparently *more* sensitive to the poison than they had been before. Richet expressed his surprise when he stated, " Then an unforseen phenomenon presented itself, which to us appeared extraordinary."

At first he could not believe that the death of these dogs had any relation to what he had done. But repeated trials always gave the same result, and Richet was forced against his own belief to the discovery of anaphylaxis, the process of becoming sensitized to some foreign material and then reacting violently if even a small quantity of this material enters the body. Today we know that anaphylaxis occurs for some people even with the use of life-saving drugs. Persons who have been found to react violently to continuous treatment with penicillin, for instance, carry cards warning doctors not to use penicillin (in the event that these persons should be brought to a hospital in a state of unconsciousness).

6. Only one more example will be given. The disease diabetes has plagued man for thousands of years, but its cause was not understood until comparatively recent years. The first break came in 1889. Professors Von Mehring and Minkowski of Strasbourg (then in Germany, now a part of France) were studying the pancreas as a digestive gland. They reasoned that one way of finding out exactly what part this gland plays in digestion was to remove the entire gland from a living animal and see how this affects the digestive process. After some difficulty, they finally succeeded in removing the entire pancreas from several dogs.

Later on, the assistant in charge of care and feeding the animals made a peculiar observation. He noticed swarms of flies hovering around the cages of the dogs which had had the operation, while the other dogs did not seem to attract so many flies. Fortunately, the assistant did not dismiss this observation as trivial. He called it to the attention of Professor Minkowski. Why should the flies be attracted to these cages? Minkowski decided to test the urine of the dogs. He discovered that the dogs which had been operated on had sugar in their urine, while the other dogs did not. The flies had been drawn to the sugar. But more important — *removal of the pancreas had caused the dogs to develop diabetes!*

Thus, the chance observation that flies were attracted to the cages of dogs whose pancreas had been removed provided the first clue to the cause of diabetes, and a scientific investigation, aimed at learning something about digestion, ended up by pointing out the relationship between the pancreas and diabetes. It remained for Frederick G. Banting and Charles H. Best to show in 1922 that the pancreas produces the hormone insulin which is essential for the proper use of sugar by the body. If insulin is lacking or insufficient, diabetes results.

Only a few cases of serendipity have been described. There are many more — too many to mention in this book, and for each case which led to a great discovery, there are dozens which led nowhere. Not every strange event or unusual observation in the laboratory leads to the pot of gold at the end of the rainbow. In fact, most of them do not lead anywhere. They are blind alleys in the maze of research. The ones we hear about are the exceptional cases which lead to great scientific discoveries.

The important thing is that unexpected things *do* happen, and that, sometimes, they *do* lead to important discoveries. Someone once said that the scientist must be alert for the unexpected while he is watching for the expected. Once the unexpected does happen, it is necessary to grasp the significance of what has occurred, and follow up the clue.

9 Inspiration— The "Educated Guess"

Have you ever studied very hard for a test, only to find that one problem continues to get you down? You can't seem to solve it. It just doesn't make sense. You work at it, try it over and over again, but with no results. Finally you give up in disgust and turn to something else. Suddenly, in the middle of your new activity, you get a hunch about the difficult problem. It is as though a flash of light hit your brain. You examine the problem again, apply your hunch, and the problem is solved — easily. You say to yourself, "This was so simple! I wonder why I didn't see it before!"

If ever you have had such an experience, it might be said that you have had a *flash of inspiration.* Your "subconscious mind" was really hard at work finding connections between the facts which you had stored in your brain. You were not even aware of the process, but all the while your brain was assembling the facts, organizing them into usable form, and suddenly — FLASH! — you are able to make a good guess. Don't worry about your failure to solve a problem at first try. You are in good company. The same thing has happened to many other people; and scientists are no exception.

As a matter of fact, many a scientific problem has been solved with the help of a hunch or an "educated guess." A scientist who is literally "up to his ears" in a problem may play a hunch, and come out with an answer. Don't get the idea that such a hunch is a wild guess. Rather it is an *educated* guess. Usually, the man who makes such a guess has already collected many facts, which he has stored in his brain. He begins to organize the facts. Seemingly isolated facts may fall into their proper places, and the man ventures a guess as to the solution of the problem. So you see, these educated guesses are based on accumulated information. Of course, nine times out of ten the hunch may be wrong. But there is always the tenth time when the educated guess leads to a correct solution.

For example, consider the case of a young high school girl who was spending her summer at the Jackson Memorial Laboratory in Bar Harbor, Maine. At the laboratory she studied heredity in mice. She bred mice, fed mice, watched mice, and read about mice — because the Jackson Memorial Laboratory is famous the world over for its carefully bred pure strains of mice. One particular strain was rather sickly and weak, and as this young lady observed the mice, she had a hunch. She was struck with the similarity of the symptoms shown by these mice to the symptoms of a terrible human disease known as muscular dystrophy. She mentioned her hunch to the scientists under whose guidance she was working, and when it was checked, it turned out that the girl had been correct. Here was a strain of mice suffering from a condition exactly like muscular dystrophy. For the first time, now, scientists had available for study an animal with muscular dystrophy — an animal which could be used for experimental study of the disease and its treatment. This animal became available because a certain high school girl had made an "educated guess."

It often happens, as in the following example, that the solution to a difficult problem comes as a flash of inspiration. Friedrich August Kekulé von Stradonitz was a famous German chemist. He lived during the latter half of the nineteenth century, when the science of organic chemistry was in its infancy. The chemists of the day knew about atoms, and they knew that complex organic molecules were made up of atoms connected in long chains. They also were aware of many organic substances which just did not fit this pattern, and no one knew why.

Kekulé was writing a textbook on chemistry, and the "irregular" organic substances were giving him trouble. How could he describe these substances to somebody else, when he himself could not understand them? He muddled over the problem for hours without any sensible solution. He became worried and depressed, and his writing failed to satisfy him. Finally he gave up. He turned his chair away from his writing toward his fireplace, and stared into the fire. As he stared, and worried over his problem, he became drowsy and soon dozed off. Even in his sleep the problem continued to torment him. He saw atoms of all sorts flit by. Tantalizingly, some of these atoms arranged themselves into long chains right before his eyes. The chains began to twist and turn and wriggle like so many snakes. They seemed to be making fun of him, teasing him, tormenting him. Suddenly in his dream Kekulé saw one of these snakes seize its own tail in its mouth and whirl around and around. . . He awoke with a start.

Here is how Kekulé himself described what followed. "As though from a flash of lightning, I awoke. I occupied the rest of the night in working out the consequence of the hypothesis." During his fitful sleep had come that sudden flash of inspiration. The molecules of these unusual compounds were not arranged in straight lines (like normal snakes) but rather in the form of a ring (like a snake with his tail in his mouth). In this way, Kekulé discovered the idea of the ring compound (Figure 9) — an idea which explains the structure of many organic compounds.

Many other discoveries have been made after a sudden flash of inspiration. Don't, however, get the idea that inspiration always comes at night when a person is asleep. It may come at any time, but, usually, bright ideas do not make themselves felt when a person is hard at work or fatigued. Rather, they are apt to occur during a period of relaxation — when you are dozing or sleeping, taking a bath, strolling in the country, or engaged in some pleasant, restful activity. Usually these flashes of inspiration follow a period of intense work, when progress seems to be at a standstill. The

FIGURE **9.** *The famous scientist Kekulé had a flash of inspiration while dozing before a fire. The molecules of organic compounds that did not fit the " chain " theory must be arranged in a complete ring, similar to snakes with their tails in their mouths!*

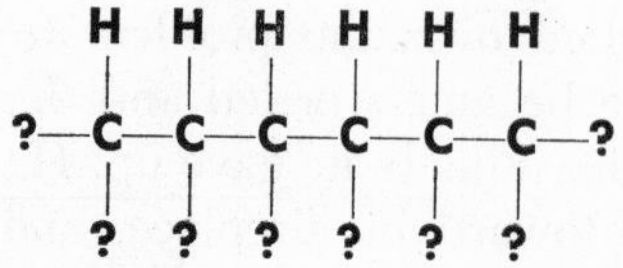

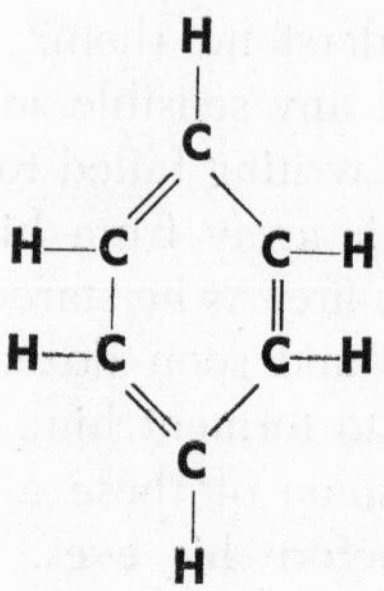

problem is temporarily dropped for some relaxing activity — and then, seemingly from nowhere, the lightning suddenly strikes!

A word of caution, however, is necessary. Unlike lightning, which may strike the same point twice, flashes of inspiration are rare, and they rarely strike twice. They can also vanish as quickly as they appear. They may come while one is dozing in the evening, but by morning be completely forgotten.

A story is told about Professor Otto Loewi, who was hard at work on the problem of how nerves cause muscles to respond. He had a hunch that chemical messengers were produced by the nerve endings, but he could not think of a way to carry out the crucial experiment to prove this. He racked his brain. He worried about it. He lived with the problem before him at all times. The more he thought about it, however, the further away he seemed to be from a solution. How could he experiment? What experiment would back up his " educated guess "?

One night he suddenly awoke from a sound sleep. Clearly he saw the solution to his problem. It was really so simple! He made a few hasty notes and went back to sleep, happy in the thought that his troubles were over. But alas, when he awoke in the morning he could not decipher his notes. The beautifully simple experiment had vanished into thin air. He spent all day trying to remember what he had to do, but it was in vain. He was as much in the dark as ever. Fortunately, the lightning struck again on another night, when he was dozing. This time Loewi got up and wrote everything down with great care. The very next day he went to the laboratory to test his theory. The experiment worked successfully, and set Loewi off on the track to a Nobel Prize, which he won in 1936.

So, if you are fortunate enough to be struck by the lightning of inspiration, it is advisable to carry the project out at once or write down *immediately* and *carefully* all the details of your inspiration. Even if the inspiration strikes you in the dead of night — write it down or take appropriate action. Tomorrow may be too late. You can't expect to be as lucky as Professor Loewi, for whom the lightning struck twice!

10 A Visit to a Science Fair

The first part of this book described some of the fundamental methods of science. It explained what is meant by "scientific methods," and it described several different ways in which information is obtained by scientists. After reading it, you may very well say, "Yes! I now know how great discoveries were made by men like Jenner, Richet, Roentgen, Fleming, Leeuwenhoek, and others. But how do *I* get started?"

Certainly your objection is justified. So far we have dealt only with basic methods. Now, however, we will get down to "brass tacks" by telling you exactly how to get started. We will outline, step by step, everything which *you* must do to begin some kind of project or investigation and carry it through to a successful conclusion.

So, grab your hat. Let's start by going down to the science fair to look over some of the projects which other pupils have done. Maybe you will get some ideas of your own. What was that? You don't know what a science fair is? Well, it's a kind of show, like a county fair. You know that at the county fair all the farmers of the county display the best things they produced on their farms — the biggest pumpkins, the finest flowers, the fanciest hens, the tastiest jams, the fattest pigs. In the same way, science pupils meet to display their best projects at a local science fair, or at a state science fair, or perhaps even at the National Science Fair.

Now you want to know what a project is. Does it mean something *big*? Well, not necessarily. Does it mean something *new*? No, not necessarily. Does it mean an *experiment*? No, not necessarily. It might mean all of these; and yet, on the other hand, it need not mean any of them. When we speak of a project, we mean *something that you do; something that you design; something that you make or build* in contrast to something that you read about, or something that you study, or something that you buy.

When you read about an experiment, you are not doing a project. On the other hand, when you have finished reading about it, if you take the time and effort to set up and carry out a similar experiment, then you are doing a project. If you learn about a piece of apparatus, or if you handle it or even work with it in school, you are not doing a project. If, however, after you have seen the apparatus, you go home and design something like it, or build something like it, you are doing a project. If you learn a scientific principle in school or from a book, you are not doing a project. But if you make a chart which illustrates or explains this principle, or if you make something which applies this principle, then you are doing a project.

So you see, a project requires that you *do* something. It can be something big or something small; something complex or something simple; something new or an old idea repeated. But here we are at the fair. Let's go in and see what is happening. Maybe we can learn more about projects by actually examining some that other boys and girls have done.

We walk into a large hall. All about us are long tables divided into smaller sections. Each section has a project on display — a project produced by a boy or girl of your age. We look closer. Some of the projects are the work of individuals; some are the work of groups. Some were done by high school pupils; others by junior high school pupils. Why, here is one done by a kindergarten class! There are complicated projects and simple ones; polished jobs and rough ones. All, however, have one thing in common. Each project is something made by a boy or a girl to express a scientific principle — a scientific idea which the pupil has learned in school or which he has read about somewhere else.

Look! Here is a working model of a steam engine. Notice that the scientific principle on which it is based is explained by a set of charts drawn in India ink. They show step by step how the steam generated in the boiler drives a piston which makes a wheel go round — and thus work is done. Here is a model homemade weather station, just as it was set up on the roof of the school by the pupils of a general science class. Look, they have an anemometer, a weather vane, a rain gauge, a barometer, and a few other things. Each instrument was designed and built by a different pupil. To prove that they work, the students have the records which were kept. See them on the wall behind the instruments — records of temperature, wind speed, air pressure, and rainfall.

Over at this end we see a girl busily cleaning a cage of white rats. Let's go a bit closer. Oh yes, she has done a nutrition experiment to see if feeding rats a single grain provides a satisfactory diet. Look at the cage of the animals which had a complete diet — the control group. The rats are active and lively. Their fur is clean and smooth. Then look at the miserable little animals in the experimental cage — those which were fed only oats. They are just lying there listlessly. Their fur is rough, their eyes are half closed and crusty. Oh yes — here are large charts with graphs of the weight gains of the two groups. What a difference in growth!

Here is a model of a volcano, and a drawing to show how it works. Now the boy who made it is demonstrating. He throws in some chemicals, and suddenly there is an eruption. Next to him is another boy with a homemade direction-finding apparatus. Over here is a wheel with several plants attached to it. The wheel is going round and round without stopping. Let's find out what this is all about. We can ask the girl who is standing nearby. Obviously it is her project.

Look at this beautiful painting in the next booth. It is entitled "The Record of the Rocks," and it shows in brilliant poster colors the gradual increase in the complexity of animals as shown by fossil remains in successive layers of rock.

Here is an interesting project called "Animals I Have Cleared." It consists of a collection of bottles, each containing a small animal — a frog, a chick, a fish, a lizard. Each animal has been treated in such a way that the tissues have become completely transparent. The bones within have been stained. On a chart in back is a description of the method that was used. You can copy the technique if you like.

Now look at this collection of teaching charts prepared by the Chart Club of one high school. Each chart is drawn in color on chart cloth and is designed so that it can be rolled up for easy storage. This is an exceptionally useful project, because after the fair the charts can become a permanent addition to the teaching collection of the school.

There is a diorama entitled "Strip Mining." It is a three-dimensional view of an area which is being worked by miners. It looks like a stage on which the action is taking place. Whoever made it was very ingenious. He used small pieces of twigs and plants for trees and shrubs, and small dolls for people. He even has a toy steam shovel in the act of ripping out a section of the hillside.

What's this one? It looks simple enough. Why, it is nothing more complicated than a shell collection. See, each shell is mounted separately, and each is named and classified. The girl even looked up the scientific names. What do you think *Ostrea virginica* is? Nothing but the common oyster!

Now what is this over here? It looks like a picture gallery. Evidently it is a separate section of the fair especially set apart for "camera-bugs." It is an exhibition of nature photographs and other photographs which illustrate science principles. Anybody with a camera can enter the competition. Look at that shot of a butterfly on a flower. You can even see the butterfly's tongue reaching deep into the flower to get the nectar. This one entitled "Lightning" is very effective. It shows a zigzag streak of lightning in a black sky, with a house silhouetted in front.

And so it goes. We can see dozens of different kinds of projects — individual projects and group projects, biology projects and chemistry projects, construction projects and experimental projects, astronomy projects and geology projects. There is no end to the variety. There are techniques and there are models. There are collections and there are experiments. There are dioramas and there are charts. There are photographs and there are paintings. There are living things and there are preserved specimens. Almost anything goes.

What was that question? Can you do a project? Of course you can! Anybody can do a project — anybody who has the interest and desire! All you have to do is *want* to do it, and the rest is easy. Naturally, you must decide what you want to do. That comes first. You must have an idea that you want to illustrate, or a question that you want to answer. Such ideas keep popping up in your science class, or as a result of your outside reading, and all you have to do is keep your eyes and ears open, and pick the one which interests you.

Once you have decided on the idea, the next job is to gather information about it. Use your science book; go to the library; ask your science teacher; discuss it with your father. Find out all there is to know about the thing you want to do, then make your specific plans. Planning is a very important step which must come before doing the project. Try to anticipate any problems which may arise. Go over your plans with your teacher. He may be able to suggest things which never occurred to you. If you rush right into the project, you may make mistakes which ruin the value of your work.

Lastly, when you have decided that your plan is as perfect as you can get it, gather together all the materials you need and go to work. Finish your project, whatever it is, and bring it to class. If it is a good project, you may want to display it at the next science fair. So, while you are working, you may as well do a good job, because *if it is worth doing at all it is worth doing well.* Do the kind of job that the judges will like when they consider and rate the projects on display at the fair.

Did you notice that some of the projects at the fair were awarded prizes? The judges were around before the display was opened to the public. They selected what they thought were the best projects in the exhibit. Of course, projects done by kindergarten groups are not compared with those done by junior high school pupils. Each age group competes on its own level. The factors which make a good project, however, remain the same at all levels. Let us therefore consider what makes a good project. What do the judges look for?

There is no single item on which you can put your finger and say, "*This* is what makes a project good." There are many things. The list which follows contains a number of suggestions for making a good project. Perhaps if you follow some of these suggestions, the project which you prepare for your science class may turn out to be good enough to display at a science fair, or even to win a prize.

1. Is your project a "crowd-stopper"? Does your project catch the eye and hold the interest? Will it make people say, "What's that one? I must look at it." Remember that your project will be but one of dozens, or hundreds, or thousands. If you don't want it to be overlooked in the crowd, you must do something to make people notice it. What can you do? Color is one idea; color attracts people. Making something with working parts is another idea; people like to push buttons and operate things. Living animals help; everyone likes to stop and look at rabbits or chickens or white rats.

2. Is your project attractive? Once you have stopped the crowd, will they continue to look, or will they turn away with the comment, "What a sloppy job!"? A little advice from your art teacher will help you in making an attractive project. Go to your art teacher with a rough layout, and ask for suggestions for dressing it up.

3. Does your project have an interesting, attractive title?
Just as the headline on a newspaper article is intended to draw your interest, and make you want to read the article, so the title of your project should attract spectators. When they read the mimeographed program, listing the projects on display, they should be intrigued by your title, and they should want to find the exhibit.

Make sure that the lettering you use for the sign over your project does not spoil your whole exhibit. Many a nice project has been made messy-looking by sloppy printing. If you cannot print well, you might consider buying ready-made letters to paste up into your title. Such letters come in all sizes and many different printing styles. They are available in all art supply stores.

4. Does your project tell a story? Does your project present a *single, simple idea?* Or is it a hodgepodge of many things? Will a person who looks at it say at once, " I see what he is trying to show," or will he say, " How confusing! I wonder what it is all about." One simple idea, clearly demonstrated, is far better than many ideas rolled up into a confusing package.

5. Does the story which your project tells illustrate a scientific principle or a science fact? Remember that this is a science fair, and that any project presented here must have some relationship to science. Remember also to ask yourself whether the principle or fact you are demonstrating is really worthwhile.

6. Is your science fact or principle presented accurately? The most attractive project in the world is a waste of time if the information it gives is inaccurate. Correct science is basic to a good project. You can be sure of accuracy if you check all your information ahead of time by referring to the proper sources of information.

7. Is your project presented in an original way? Try to think of a new way of presenting the idea you are trying to get across. It may be all right in some cases to repeat the work of someone else exactly as he did it, but in doing this you are not showing your own personality in your work. A novel twist, a new approach, calls attention to your own ability and thus makes a better project.

8. Is your project well constructed? Will it be easy for you to transport your project to the place where the fair is to be held? Will it be a simple task for you to set it up at the fair? (Many fairs require that the exhibitor set up his project without outside help.)

Will it fit in the space allotted to you? Will the exhibit stand up for the duration of the fair? Is it strong enough and sturdy enough to withstand the handling it may receive from the visitors at the fair? If there are any delicate parts, or breakable parts, or valuable parts, are they well protected? Will it be easy to take the exhibit apart again at the conclusion of the fair? Will you still have, at the end of the fair, all the parts you brought with you at the beginning? All these questions should be taken into consideration when you *plan* your project as well as when you build it.

9. Does your project require special care?   Many projects require special attention for the duration of the fair. If this care is not provided, the project may begin to deteriorate. If yours is a project requiring special care, have you made the preparations which are necessary? If you have living animals, will they be fed and cleaned at the correct times? How will they be protected against mishandling by the visiting crowds? Will your plants be watered regularly, or will they be allowed to wilt and droop? If you have made a working model of some kind, will it be kept in working order? Will bulbs and batteries be replaced when they burn out? Will connections be repaired when they break? How will you protect small parts or valuable parts against people who like to take home souvenirs?

10. Does your project meet the conditions specified by the directors of the science fair?   Here is an actual statement taken from the rules of a science fair which was held recently.

Your project will be judged based on the following criteria:

a. The exhibit should illustrate some aspect of pure or applied science.

b. Scientific approach — it should demonstrate the result of analysis, experimentation, observation, and verification in the solution of a clearly defined scientific problem.

c. Uniqueness of concept — the ideas should be original, in keeping with the age level of the exhibitor.

d. Use of materials — common, everyday materials should be used, where possible, in the preparation of the exhibits.

e. Thoroughness — exhibits should be complete within the scope of the problem and the age level of the exhibitor.

f. Technical skill — the exhibit should show skillful workmanship.

g. Dramatic value — the exhibit and presentation should be dynamic and graphic.

h. Social implication — exhibitors should show possible contributions of their projects to human welfare.

i. Timeliness — the reason should be indicated where the exhibit and presentation are of current scientific interest.

After reading the preceding suggestions and advice, do you think you can do a good project? Of course you can! It isn't really very hard, and afterward you can even go a step further. Maybe your project can develop into an original investigation of some kind. That's what the rest of this book is about — how to carry on an investigation. The advice given in the following pages is not meant for seasoned research workers, or even for college students going into research. It is intended only for boys and girls like you, who are facing for the first time the task of carrying out an investigation.

In the pages which follow, the word *investigation* is used in a much broader sense than either *experiment* or *project*. It is used to refer to any form of systematic problem-solving, whether it be a project requiring investigation, a trial-and-error procedure, a series of planned observations, an actual controlled experiment, or plain library research. It refers to any activity which an interested pupil may be carrying on in connection with school work, as part of a science scholarship competition, in building a display at a science fair, or for his own pleasure.

Carrying out an investigation requires that certain steps be performed. These steps are listed below.

1. A problem must be selected.
2. Various preliminary preparations must be made.
3. The investigation must be planned.
4. The investigation must be carried out.
5. The observations must be recorded.
6. The data must be analyzed.
7. The conclusion must be formulated.
8. The investigation and its results must be publicized.

Each of these steps will now be considered in detail, and it is hoped that you will find helpful information for carrying out your own investigation.

11 Choosing a Problem

The first difficulty which a boy or girl faces in carrying out an investigation is finding a problem on which to work. It is not so hard for a professional research worker to find a problem, because there is usually a director of research who points the way by suggestion or by order. Furthermore, in carrying out his work, the researcher runs across many puzzling situations which cause questions to come up in his mind. Any one of these puzzling situations may give rise to several problems worthy of study. A research worker who never runs into such situations, or does not notice that such situations arise, probably won't amount to much as a researcher. Unfortunately, you and other students in school are not usually exposed to these puzzling situations. Furthermore, your knowledge of science is far more limited than that of the older research man, so you are at a decided disadvantage when it comes to locating a problem.

On the other hand, you have one advantage over the older research man. Nobody expects you to do a completely original piece of research work. Nor does anyone expect you to make a brand new discovery of great significance. You are merely expected to show that you understand and appreciate the methods of science, or that you can apply these methods to some problem, new or old. But what kind of a problem?

Perhaps you can get a better idea of the kind of problem you should choose by considering the following requirements:

1. Select a problem which deals with something of interest to you. If your favorite hobby is raising tropical fish, find a problem for investigation which deals with tropical fish. If you are a radio "ham" at heart, don't think in terms of fish for your problem, but rather think about something electrical — something which deals with vacuum tubes and circuits. If your hobby is cooking, think about ways in which to solve problems you encounter in cooking or baking.

2. Select a problem in a field with which your adviser is familiar. Naturally, your teacher, or your brother, or whoever is advising you can give you much better advice if he has a great deal of knowledge in the field. If your adviser is an expert on protozoa, he can probably give you more help with a problem on protozoa than with a problem on astronomy.

3. Select a problem which is appropriate to the purpose you have in mind. It is a good idea to ask yourself, " Why am I doing this investigation? " because the choice of a problem may be determined in part by the purpose you have in mind. If you are doing it to make a report for your science class, it may be enough to do some extensive reading, summarize what you have read, and make the report. By contrast, if you are carrying out an investigation to fulfill the requirements of a science scholarship competition, you must be sure that the problem you select meets the requirements set down in the rules. In one national science competition there is a requirement that the project have some relationship to metals. Obviously, even the best-planned and best-developed research problem which you might present would be eliminated from consideration unless it dealt in some way with metals.

4. Select a problem with which you have a good chance of accomplishing something. Everyone knows that nothing else is as encouraging as success, and nothing else as discouraging as failure. Therefore, it is important for you to select a problem which is likely to lead to a successful conclusion. It is not always easy to determine in advance that working with a certain problem will lead to a conclusion, but there are several things to keep in mind which can help you eliminate projects that are sure to go uncompleted.

a. *Will you be able to finish the investigation in the time you have at your disposal?* Suppose you have one school term in which to carry on your experiment. It would hardly be wise to plan a study of the heredity of flower color in peach trees, because you know that a peach tree planted from seed takes four or five years to produce flowers. You don't have that much time; you have a mere five months in which to work.

b. *Can this investigation be carried out with the physical facilities available to you?* Do you have the necessary space, materials, and equipment to do the experiment you are considering? For example, doing a nutrition experiment which requires thirty dogs as subjects is quite out of the question. In all probability, you are not equipped to keep thirty dogs. Your school probably can't provide the room, and unless your parents own a kennel, they would object to having so many animals around the house.

By the same token, if some very expensive chemical is required for the investigation, don't undertake it unless you can afford to lay out the money for the purchase of the chemical. Also, do not undertake a project which requires the use of a cyclotron, or an X-ray machine, unless you know in advance that such a machine is at your disposal.

c. *Do you have the necessary knowledge to carry out this particular investigation?* While it is true that knowledge can be acquired by study and reading, it is also true that at your age you may not yet be mature enough to understand everything. Much knowledge is on a level far above the ability of a pupil of your age. For example, you may not know enough advanced mathematics to carry out a project dealing with atomic physics, or with population genetics. If so, it is best not to attempt such problems.

d. *Do you have the technical skills necessary to carry out this project?* Here again, technical skills can be developed by practice. Many pupils have carried on successful projects in which it was necessary to develop highly specialized skills not ordinarily taught in school. However, there are many techniques which are far beyond the skills of even an outstanding boy or girl. Consider the chemical skills necessary to analyze a vitamin or a hormone and determine its structure. Or suppose you decide to repeat one of Pavlov's famous experiments. Are you a sufficiently capable surgeon to prepare a dog for the experiment? Here is a description in Pavlov's own words. "We have here before us a dog . . . which possesses an ordinary gastric fistula with metallic cannula, and has had its oesophagus divided as well, so that the mouth is cut off from all communication with the cavity of the stomach."

e. *Does the investigation you are considering have any dangerous aspects?* It is neither desirable nor advisable for you to carry on a project involving danger to yourself or to your fellow students. For example, you probably should not work with bacteria which cause human disease. Even though you may consider yourself an expert on bacteriology, don't work with pathogenic organisms. Remember, accidents happen even where world-famous specialists in bacteriology are at work. A number of research workers have become ill or even died as a result of accidental infection caused by the germ they were studying. By the same token, you should not undertake projects which involve poisonous animals like rattlesnakes or black widow spiders, highly inflammable substances, explosive mixtures, toxic fumes, materials that are radioactive to a dangerous degree, or other hazards. Remember — it's better to be safe than sorry!

f. *Is the investigation you are considering worthwhile?* It is rather foolish to set out to investigate something which is obvious. For example, " Do seeds need water to sprout? " might be a fine problem for a kindergarten science class, but it would hardly be considered a worthwhile problem for a junior or senior high school student. Similarly, an elaborate investigation to answer the question " Do paramecia reproduce by fission? " is a waste of valuable time for older students. Every schoolboy (including the experimenter) knows the answer in advance. This is like setting up a straw man so that you can knock him down. Even as far back as 1620, Francis Bacon criticized this procedure in his *Novum Organum* when he wrote, ". . . and Aristotle himself then raises up questions at will in order to settle them."

No, it is not desirable to raise as a problem a question for which you already know the answer. A minor change in such a question, however, may make all the difference in the world. For example, it was pointed out that the question " Do paramecia reproduce by fission? " is hardly worthwhile as a research problem for a high school pupil. Suppose, though, the question is modified as follows: " What is the effect of low temperature on fission in paramecia? " This slight modification can lead to an interesting investigation, well worth doing.

Another point is worth remembering. Not all research seems worthwhile at the moment it is done. Sometimes the value of a discovery does not become evident for many years. For example, Pasteur once observed that disease bacteria poured into the soil soon disappear. Today we understand the import of this observation. We know that there are many soil organisms which produce chemicals (antibiotics, our newest " wonder drugs ") and that these in turn prevent the growth of other organisms or even kill them. Similarly, Mendel's discoveries about heredity seemed worthless until thirty-five years after they were published. So, if you have an idea, don't drop it just because somebody says it is not worthwhile. Evaluate it yourself, discuss it with your adviser, consider it thoroughly, and if you think it has possibilities, go ahead and develop the idea. Remember what the learned members of the Royal Society told Edward Jenner when he asked permission to report to them his experiments on vaccination. They did not think his idea was worthwhile, but how wrong they were!

How do you go about getting an idea for a project or for a research problem? The secret is *not* to go about it at all. It is not a good idea to sit down for the purpose of dreaming up a problem. Rather, the best problems arise of their own accord as a result of something you read, or something you do, or something you see. Things are going on all around you. Significant events are taking place all the time. People are doing things; you are seeing things;

FIGURE **10.** *Things are constantly happening all around you. If you miss them, as this boy is doing, you may miss an opportunity to study an interesting problem. Practice observing!*

hearing things. If you keep your eyes and ears open, and your mind alert (Figure 10), you are sure to run into many situations which puzzle you. Any one of these puzzling situations might be the basis for a research problem. For example, consider these incidents:

1. One day there was an informal discussion in the gymnasium of a junior high school. The topic was fat and muscle. "A fat boy is heavier than a muscular boy of the same size," said the instructor. One young man was not satisfied. He went home with a scientific problem to solve — " Which is heavier — muscle or fat? " Before he knew it, he was hard at work on a basic research problem. He found his problem by keeping his ears (and his mind) open.

2. A girl who raised hamsters read all she could about them, and one day she learned that in their wild state, hamsters go into hibernation when winter comes. This was a surprise to her, because her own pets didn't hibernate during winter, but went on living quite actively all year round. A question therefore arose in her mind — " Why? " When she discussed it with her science teacher, he suggested that this was a wonderful research problem for her. The girl had never thought of it as a potential problem for research, but once she got started, found that there were many interesting aspects to be followed up. For example, was it the gradual drop in temperature which made the animals curl up and go to sleep, or was it the gradual shortening of the day as the sun set earlier and earlier with the onset of winter? Also, what difference is there between two rodents like the rat and the hamster, which makes the hamster hibernate in winter while the rat remains active? As you can see, this girl found several problems growing out of a single question which arose in her mind while she was reading about hamsters and observing her pets.

3. A boy for the first time in his life became the proud owner of a dog. One day his dog got into a fight with another dog, and came crawling home to "lick his wounds." The boy was upset by the gashes in the skin of his pet. He was ready to put iodine and bandages on the dog, when his father stopped him. " Leave him alone. He'll be all right," said the father. " But won't he get infections? " asked the boy. " No," said the father. " He'll keep the wounds clean by licking them." The boy saw the animal lick his wounds, and after a while they healed. This gave the youngster reason to pause and think. " Can it be that there is something in the saliva of a dog which kills germs? Something like penicillin?" Thus arose a wonderful problem for study — does dog saliva have antibiotic qualities? It all started with an ordinary incident in everyday life. Of course, the boy had to learn how to raise bacteria and handle them in order to solve the problem, but that is a story in itself.

4. Another boy, an outstanding mathematics student, wished to become a doctor. In his search for a biological or medical problem on which to work for a science scholarship competition, he came into the biology laboratory to discuss the matter with his former biology teacher. "I can't get a single good idea for a research problem," he complained. The conversation was temporarily interrupted while the teacher took care of some other matter, and in the meantime the boy looked around the laboratory. He noticed a cage containing mice of several different colors — black, brown, gray, white. "Gee! What would happen," asked the boy, "if all these mice mated at random in the cage?" The teacher happened to overhear the question. "There's your problem," he said. "It's a problem in population genetics, and I wouldn't suggest it to anyone except a mathematics genius like you. Suppose you work out a theoretical formula for predicting the population ten 'mouse generations' later, and then do the experiment to see whether your formula predicts accurately. Look up the Hardy-Weinberg equilibrium." The boy went home that day with enough of a problem to keep himself occupied for some time. It all arose from a chance observation in the laboratory.

5. A certain young tropical fish enthusiast made a strange observation in his tanks. In one tank, a certain plant grew large and luxuriously, while in another tank the identical plant remained small and stunted. "Why should this be?" he wondered. He went to an expert at the aquarium supply store, where the man mumbled something about the pH of the water. This made the boy even more curious. A chemistry teacher explained to him that pH referred to the acidity of the water. "Does this mean that the more acid the nature of the water is, the less the plant grows?" asked the boy. "I don't know," answered the teacher, "but why don't you do an experiment to find out?" Here is a case where a boy found a problem in his own fish tank. No doubt, other boys and girls have made the same observation without following it up; thus, they lost the opportunity of doing a worthwhile piece of research.

6. One day a girl whose father was in the button business heard him talk about making artificial mother-of-pearl buttons. "How do you get them to shine like that?" she asked. "Oh, we mix in some stuff that we buy from a chemical concern," he said. "The chemist tells me they make it from the scales of fish." The girl was amazed. She began to wonder about how fish scales could yield a substance with such sheen. She ended up with an interesting research project.

From these examples it should be quite obvious to you that the easiest way to find yourself a research problem is to be observant and inquisitive. Always look for the "why" and the "how" of the things about you, and many problems will come your way. However, don't forget to measure each problem against the standards listed earlier in this chapter.

Perhaps it will help you select your problem if you know what problems have been completed by other students of your age. For this reason, the next chapter presents a number of typical problems. Some were done for science scholarship competitions, some for science fairs, some for class projects. They are classified under different headings, but they all have one thing in common: they have been carried out by boys and girls of your age. If other pupils can find such problems and carry on investigations to solve them, *you can, too.*

Before you look at the next chapter, however, you should know about an incident from the life of Professor Ira Remsen. Professor Remsen was a famous chemist who discovered, among other things, the substance *saccharine,* which is often used as a substitute for sugar. For many years he taught chemistry at Johns Hopkins University, and later he became president of that university.

Even a famous man begins life like anybody else, and the Remsen story goes back to the days when Ira Remsen was just a young boy earning a few pennies by helping out in a doctor's office. He was very curious about many of the things he saw and heard, so curious that he often read textbooks to find out more about the mysteries of science — but read the story for yourself, as Ira Remsen told it.

While reading a textbook of chemistry, I came upon the statement "nitric acid acts upon copper." I was getting tired of reading such absurd stuff and I determined to see what this meant. Copper was more or less familiar to me, for copper cents were then in use. I had seen a bottle marked "nitric acid" on a table in the doctor's office where I was then "doing time." I did not know its peculiarities, but I was getting on and likely to learn. The spirit of adventure was upon me.

Having nitric acid and copper, I had only to learn what the words "acts upon" meant. . . . All was still. In the interest of knowledge I was even willing to sacrifice one of the few copper cents then in my possession.

I put one of them on the table; opened the bottle marked "nitric acid"; poured some of the liquid on the copper; and prepared to take an observation. But what was this wonderful thing I beheld? The cent was already changed, and it was no small change either. A greenish blue liquid foamed and fumed over the cent and over the table. The air in the neighborhood of the performance became colored dark red. This was disagreeable and suffocating. How should I stop this?

I tried to get rid of the objectionable mess by picking it up and throwing it out of the window, which I had meanwhile opened. I learnt another fact — nitric acid not only acts on copper but it acts upon fingers. The pain led to another unpremeditated experiment. I drew my fingers across my trousers and another fact was discovered. Nitric acid acts upon trousers.

Taking everything into consideration that was the most impressive experiment . . . I ever performed. . . . It resulted in a desire on my part to learn more about that remarkable kind of action. Plainly, the only way to learn about it was to see its results, to experiment, to work in a laboratory.*

Ira Remsen's experiment illustrates one of the basic ideas of scientific method — that direct observation is the best way to answer a question. But in choosing his problem and carrying it out, Ira Remsen the boy did many things which would have shocked Ira Remsen the famous scientist. Reread the list of standards against which a problem for a boy or girl should be measured. How do you think Ira Remsen's problem would stand up against these criteria? Now do you see why Professor Remsen would have been shocked? If you do, you are ready to go on to Chapter 12.

---

* From *Life of Ira Remsen,* by F. H. Getman, Chemical Education Publishing Company, Easton, Pa. The selection quoted above appears on pages 9–10 of this book and is used with permission of the publisher.

12 A Classification of Problem Types

It is truly amazing to see the wide variety of problems which have been tackled by boys and girls like you. Study any list of student projects, read any summary of student investigations, and you will see that there is no limit to the interests and imagination of our American youth. You will realize at once that problems can be drawn from every field of science beginning with astronomy and ending with zoology. There are philosophical problems and practical ones; construction jobs and inventions; experimental research problems and library studies; broad surveys and problems of limited scope; simple projects and complex, technical investigations. In short, almost anything goes, as long as it is interesting, stimulating, and worthwhile.

Classifying these widely varied experiments, projects, and other investigations is an almost impossible task. Still, it is worth having such a classification, even though we know that it cannot possibly be complete and accurate. We will therefore make a try at classifying problems which former students have studied. Some of these problems may involve topics with which you are not familiar. Look these topics up in an encyclopedia, a dictionary, a science reference book, or ask your teacher about them. Finding out what they are may give you an unusual idea for your own work.

Try to decide which of the problems have been well stated and which have not. Later you will have an opportunity to criticize the manner in which these student problems were stated.

1. Problems of historic nature. Under this heading might fall any activity which repeats a famous experiment originally carried out by a scientist of the past, or the building of a model of some famous piece of equipment which was used by a scientific worker of the past. We also might include investigations which take an old idea and test it to see if it has any value in the light of present-day knowledge. A few examples are:

a. Inheritance in peas; an experimental re-examination of Mendel's work.
b. Do cobwebs really have antiseptic value?
c. A Tyndall box which works.
d. Constructing a Leeuwenhoek microscope.
e. Graphical development of the sieve of Eratosthenes.
f. A treatise on Euler's lines.
g. Are Schleiden and Schwann really the authors of the " cell theory "?
h. The description of Redi's experiment, as given in my biology textbook, compared with the real thing.
i. The scientific work of Benjamin Franklin.
j. Archimedes' principle rediscovered.
k. The development of lighter-than-air craft.
l. Does walking under a ladder bring hard luck?
m. Does saliva have antibiotic qualities? — experiments with dog saliva.

2. Making a collection. Naturally, collecting for the sake of collecting is hardly a scientific undertaking. To be of any value, from the point of view of science, a collection must be so arranged and organized that it tells a story — a story of scientific interest and value. Here are a few examples:

a. A collection of seeds from the area around the school.
b. A census of breeding birds in the Jones Beach area. [New York City]
c. The fresh-water algae of Central Park lake. [New York City]
d. What you can find at low tide.
e. A collection of giant crystals grown from solution.
f. The form of snowflakes as photographed by special techniques.
g. A collection of spider webs.
h. My seaweed collection.
i. A collection of all the plants which appeared in a backyard plot one foot square.
j. Humor in science — a collection of cartoons.
k. Biology and design — a collection of materials with biological motifs.

3. Designing and building a piece of apparatus or equipment. There is no limit to the number of different kinds of apparatus and equipment which pupils can build out of cheap and easily obtainable materials. Of course, building such a piece of equipment requires that you first understand the basic principles underlying its operation. The thing you are building might be as simple as a water wheel, or as complex as a Tesla coil or a cloud chamber. Whatever it is, it must work. Here are a few examples:

    a. A working model of a subsonic wind tunnel.
    b. A television camera.
    c. A continuous cloud chamber.
    d. An artificial heart for tissue culture.
    e. Experiments with a homemade oscillograph.
    f. High temperature experiments with a homemade electric furnace.
    g. The design of some simple " thinking " machines.
    h. The construction of a six-inch Newtonian reflecting telescope.
    i. A tick-tack-toe machine.
    j. Experiments with my seismograph.
    k. A working model of a mechanical weed puller.
    l. A sensitive Geiger counter made at home.
    m. The weather station on my roof.
    n. A working model of a volcano.
    o. The vacuum tube Tesla coil.
    p. Construction and use of a micro-manipulator.

4. Testing or standardizing a product. No doubt you have heard a wide variety of claims for the hundreds of products which are advertised over radio and television. Well, which tooth paste *is* the best? *Can* a cleansing tissue really kill germs as claimed? Here is material for unlimited research. Consider these investigations which have already been tried by others:

    a. Does monosodium glutamate actually improve the taste of food?
    b. Do tooth pastes kill mouth bacteria?
    c. A comparison of No. 120 film produced by different companies.
    d. Testing the effectiveness of four different insecticides against the common housefly.

e. Comparing the effectiveness of six different cigarette filters which are available on the market.

f. A comparison of hydrogenated shortenings.

g. Six brands of dog food compared.

h. Does fluorinated tooth paste stop tooth decay?

i. A comparison of the vitamin C content of Florida and California oranges at different seasons of the year.

j. How much antibiotic added to fish food is safe for tropical fish?

k. Budding in yeast as affected by the amount of sugar in solution.

l. The effects of soaps and detergents on tensile strength of fabrics.

m. What is the effect of injecting *Hyponex* into dwarf marigolds?

n. Determining the amount of reducing sugars in various beers.

o. The advantages and disadvantages of various forms of lighting.

5. Developing a new product, or a new use for an existing product. There is an old saying that "there is nothing new under the sun." Still, new products are constantly appearing, and new uses are invariably being found for standard products. Perhaps you too can seek a new product, or a new use for one that is familiar. Other pupils have done so. Here are a few illustrations:

a. Using science to produce a better pillow.

b. A photoelectric phonograph cartridge.

c. A versatile intercommunication system.

d. A new type of space station.

e. Using detergents to help baked goods retain their freshness.

f. The antibiotic qualities of onion juice and garlic juice.

g. Producing seedless tomatoes by treatment with plant hormones.

h. A new design for an airfoil.

i. The use of red cabbage juice and grape juice as indicators.

j. Food from the sea — algae as human food.

k. Hydrolysis of wood into fermentable sugars.

l. Obtaining alcohol from orange peels.

m. Dehydrated elodea as a new food supplement.

6. Finding a new or better technique for accomplishing something. The fact that something has been done in a certain way for a long time does not necessarily mean that this is the best or most efficient way to do it. Perhaps you can find a better way of doing something. It *is* possible. Here is evidence in the form of the titles of several student investigations of this type.

a. Injecting fertilizers instead of putting them into the soil.
b. Using paper chromatography to identify amino acids.
c. Killing bacteria with ultrasonic sounds.
d. Stimulating plant growth with vitamins and antibiotics.
e. Inducing mutations in plants with electricity.
f. Improving reception in crystal detectors.
g. An attempt to replace the gelatin in photographic emulsions with a synthetic resin.
h. A suggested new system of writing for the blind.
i. Improving the calendar.
j. Pictures in poor light with hypersensitization.
k. Dwarfing garden plants with chemicals.
l. A novel technique for trisecting an angle.
m. A special use of the slide rule to solve equations.

7. Describing a natural phenomenon. The original natural philosophers of several centuries ago were really the forerunners of our modern scientists. They spent a great deal of their time in observing and describing the things which went on about them. Even though science has advanced mightily since those days, there is still much work to be done in observing nature and in describing the natural phenomena that are always about us. Many of your fellow students have done interesting work with this sort of activity, as the following titles show:

a. Studying the sunspots on the sun.
b. The reactions of frogs to chemical and electrical stimuli.
c. A study of extrasensory perception.
d. Do ants leave trails?
e. Observations on the variable stars.
f. The parasites found in perch caught in Lake Champlain.
g. The effect of overcrowding on the growth and reproduction of fish.
h. X-ray observations of the stomach of a rabbit.
i. Pothole erosion in the Yosemite region.
j. Regeneration in Planaria.

k. Phenocopies in Drosophila.

l. A comparison of vertebrate eyes.

m. The migration of the cottontail rabbit.

n. The twenty-one day miracle — chick embryology.

8. Demonstrating a scientific principle in action. In your study of science at school, you have learned many basic principles. Many wonderful projects can be built around these principles. It takes only a little imagination to go from the basic idea to a problem which arises out of it. From there it is only one step further to a project, experiment, or other investigation. Here are some samples:

a. The mechanism of muscle action.

b. The study of crystallography.

c. An electric penny-tossing machine for testing the " law of chance."

d. Determining the growth curve of guppies.

e. The effect of punishment on maze learning.

f. Illustration and proof of the laws of motion.

g. My work on the equation $ax^2 \pm b = y^2$.

h. An analysis of the " law of chance."

i. Heredity of color in parakeets.

j. A study of the mathematical principles of the quantum theory.

9. Relating a scientific principle to everyday life. The scientific principles which you learn in school are often theoretical. Yet they have practical applications in life. Many problems originate from attempts to apply these principles to worldly matters, and each problem that arises can be the beginning of a project, an experiment, an investigation, or research which will lead you into more and more interesting fields. Here are a few examples:

a. Retarding spoilage in apples.

b. The effect of weather on the sound of musical instruments.

c. What effect has cigarette smoke on the length of life of guinea pigs?

d. The absorption characteristics of filters of five different brands of cigarettes.

e. Correction of a speech problem in multiple sclerosis.

f. Control of the mosquito in the San Joaquin Valley.

g. An experiment in the elimination of crab grass.

h. Science in a tannery.

i. What is the effect of alcohol on the behavior and breeding of guinea pigs?

j. How the doctor uses blood to diagnose disease.

k. Parents! Do you learn faster than your children?

10. Broad surveys. Some projects and investigations do not fit into any of the previous categories. They are broad surveys, covering wide areas of scientific knowledge. Here are a few samples:

a. An evaluation of food advertising.

b. The effect of comic books on school children.

c. Soil erosion in the United States.

d. Investigations into the elementary theories of light.

e. A study of high school honor graduates.

f. The use of fingerprints in identification.

g. An ecological study of the marine fauna of Nantucket Island, Massachusetts.

h. Speleology — the study of caves.

i. The production of silver mirrors.

j. Indian relics tell a story.

k. A critical analysis of infinity.

l. Hydroponics.

m. The migratory routes of man's ancestors.

As you see, there is a great deal of overlapping among the problems of the different classes. Some can fit very well into more than one class. Furthermore, this is not the only classification of problems which is possible. There are many others. Here are the names of two booklets which use other forms of classification:

> *Thousands of Science Projects,* by M. E. Patterson and J. H. Kraus, Science Service, 1719 N. Street N.W., Washington 6, D.C., 1953. 25¢
>
> *Student Projects,* by John H. Woodburn, Future Scientists of America, 1201 16th St. N.W., Washington 6, D.C., 1954. 50¢

Both of these booklets list many additional problems from which you can get ideas for your own project, experiment, or investigation. In addition, your science teacher can probably refer you to other lists of problems which are suitable for your age and grade level.

Whatever problem you select for your own, you must learn to state it properly. In the next chapter we will study the proper way to state a problem.

13 Stating the Problem

Once you have selected your problem, your next task is to state it simply, clearly, concisely, and in good English. This is essential so that you may have an exact notion of what it is you plan to do. One of the best ways to state the problem is in the form of a question to be answered by your investigation. However, this is not the only way. Any clear statement is satisfactory, *but the statement of the problem must be simple, clear, and concise.*

Consider the following as a proposed problem — "Antibiotics and Plants." What does it mean? Can you tell from this statement what the experimenter intends to do?

1. Does he intend to make a survey of all plants which produce antibiotics?
2. Does he plan to study how plants produce antibiotics?
3. Is it his intention to find out what kinds of antibiotics plants are able to produce?
4. Does he expect to treat plants with antibiotics to see what happens to the plants?
5. Perhaps he is trying to do something to plants, to make them produce antibiotics.
6. It is even possible that he may be working on two separate things entirely — plants on the one hand and antibiotics on the other hand.

Obviously, "Antibiotics and Plants" is a poorly defined problem, since it can be interpreted in half a dozen different ways. Let us now consider, by contrast, a problem which is clearly defined, and well stated — "What is the effect of injecting penicillin into bean plants?" No one can misunderstand the intention of the experimenter. He obviously plans to inject penicillin into bean plants to see how this will affect the plants. No other interpretation of the problem is possible. Therefore, " What is the effect of injecting penicillin into bean plants? " is a well-stated problem.

Here are a few samples of problems which are poorly stated as compared with related problems which are well stated.

Poor Statement of a Problem	Good Statement of a Problem
1. Antibiotics and plants.	1. What is the effect of injecting penicillin into bean plants?
2. Stimulating animals to grow.	2. Using a diet fortified with vitamins to stimulate growth in dogs.
3. A study of the rate of learning of parents, uncles, aunts, cousins, and other adults, as compared with children who go to high school, based on success in learning to run a maze with a stylus while blindfolded.	3. A comparison of the learning ability of adults and high school pupils, based on success with a stylus maze.
4. Plant cancer.	4. Inducing cancerous growths in sugar beets by inoculating *Bacillus tumefacens*.
5. Plants and electricity.	5. Using electricity to cause mutations in plants.
6. Study of the effect on color change in *Rana pipiens* of exposure to ultraviolet radiation and related studies of blood, etc.	6. How exposure to ultraviolet rays affects color, blood, and other traits in *Rana pipiens*.
7. Experimental research with *Drosophila melanogaster*.	7. Producing mutants of *Drosophila melanogaster* by X-ray irradiation.
8. Coloring chicks.	8. Is it possible to hatch artificially colored chicks?

9. Insecticides and insects.	9. A comparison of the effectiveness of six different insecticides on common houseflies.
10. Study of the growth and reproduction of *Paramecium caudatum* under certain environmental conditions and of some of its tropisms.	10. How changes in environmental conditions affect the growth, reproduction, and tropisms of *Paramecium caudatum*.

After you have studied these comparisons, go back to Chapter 12 and look over the sample problems listed there. Select a few at random and ask yourself, "Exactly what is the experimenter going to find out?" If you analyze these problems, you will realize that many of them are clearly defined and well stated but that many others are poorly stated and ambiguous. Try to restate the poor ones in such a way that there can be no mistaking their purpose. This will be good practice in preparation for the time when you must state your own problem.

When you do state your own problem, be sure that it gives a clear, simple, concise picture of what it is you plan to do. Write out the problem, and then ask somebody to read it and tell you what you have in mind. If your statement of the problem can pass this test, you are ready to go ahead with the first step toward solving it.

14 Preparatory Work— Locating Preliminary Readings

Once you have chosen your problem, you must find out as much as possible about it. There is nothing new in this suggestion. As long ago as 1620, Bacon wrote in his *Novum Organum:* "When anyone prepares himself for discovery, he first inquires and obtains a full account of all that has been said on the subject by others."

How do you go about finding out what others have said and done? The best way to do this is *to discuss the matter with your adviser,* and *to read as much as you can about previous work relating to or bearing directly upon your problem.* Do not restrict your reading too severely. The wider your reading, the greater will be your experience, and the easier it will be for you to correlate what you discover with what you already know.

There are certain dangers in such reading, however, and because of these dangers some scientists do not think it is always a good idea to read what other scientists have to say. They seem to think that when you read, your mind becomes conditioned along the lines of what the author says. You therefore no longer have an original viewpoint, and your own work tends to conform to what you have read. The scientists who criticize reading about the work of other scientists point out that many great discoveries in certain fields were made by men trained in other fields. For example, Pasteur (a chemist) showed the relationship between bacteria and disease (a biological problem) and Galvani (a biologist) discovered current electricity (a problem in physics). The question is whether or not these men made their discoveries mainly because they had fewer preconceived notions in a field which was somewhat less familiar to them then their own.

Another factor is that certain of the information you get in your reading may actually be incorrect. Incorrect knowledge which has become established may prove to be a real barrier to reaching the truth. For example, the established idea that " germs cause disease " was a hindrance to the discovery of the cause of diseases like pellagra. Many fruitless hours were spent hunting for a germ that caused pellagra, when no such germ exists. Established authorities insisted that there *must be* such a germ which got into the body. They could not conceive of a disease caused by the lack of something.

All of these thoughts led one famous scientist to say, " It is that which we do know, which is the greatest hindrance to our learning that which we do not know."

Despite these dangers, reading is absolutely essential. The important thing is to read with a realization of the dangers, and with an open mind. Read to get ideas. Weigh what you read, and evaluate it. Try to correlate what you read with what you know. Search for important generalizations, but at the same time look for contradictions, flaws, and questions not adequately answered. If you do this, your reading will be an asset to you, rather than a hindrance.

Where do you find the readings? This is the next question to consider. Of course, you can ask your adviser to suggest some sources of information, or you can discuss the problem with someone else who knows the field. However, there are certain standard ways of locating the preliminary readings, and it is a good idea to become familiar with them.

1. College textbooks. You might look up the subject in one or more college textbooks. Such books are good sources of information for basic material, *if they are up to date*. Take a look at the date when the book was written. Think for a moment what you would find about vitamins in a textbook written in 1920; or about antibiotics in a book written in 1940; or about atomic energy in a textbook of 1945. As a matter of fact, it is sometimes said that even the most up-to-date textbook is ten or fifteen years behind the recent research on the subject. Don't forget that textbooks may have errors or misleading statements. If you keep these cautions in mind, you will get much value from reading textbooks. Often, textbooks list the original sources upon which the contents were based. Such a list may provide you with valuable clues for further reading.

2. The *Readers' Guide to Periodical Literature*. Here is a good reference tool, issued every two weeks in the form of a pamphlet. Each issue indexes by subject matter all the articles which have appeared in about 125 magazines during the few weeks immediately preceding publication of the pamphlet. At the end of every year, all the issues of *Readers' Guide* for that year are combined into one large book, and every two years, a single volume is issued to replace the two yearly issues.

The *Readers' Guide* is arranged like a dictionary, with entries in alphabetical order. Articles are listed by author and by subject. A kind of shorthand is used, so that a great deal of information can be packed into a small space. Here is a sample entry from the October 10, 1955, issue of *Readers' Guide*.

> ADRENAL glands
> Gland of stress. J. D. Corrington, il.
> Nature Mag 48:446–8 O'55.

This entry reveals that an illustrated article about the adrenal glands, written by J. D. Corrington under the title of "Gland of Stress," appears in Volume 48 of *Nature Magazine* on pages 446–448 in the issue for October, 1955.

To show how *Readers' Guide* is used, let us assume that in March, 1958, you want to locate articles dealing with the hereditary aspects of hemophilia. You go to your school library or the public library, and start looking in *Readers' Guide* under the headings *bleeders, genetics, hemophilia, heredity, human heredity,* and any other related headings that come to mind. You start with the issue for February, 1958 (the most recent available at the time), and then you go back to the January, 1958, issue. Next, you take the single volume for 1955–1957, and if you want to go back further, the single 1953–1955 volume. *Readers' Guide* goes back to 1900.

You may find listings for many articles on hemophilia, coming from different magazines. You now have all the information you need to locate each article. All you have to do is go to the stacks in your library, select the right issue of the magazine, turn to the correct page, and read the article.

Your school librarian will be very glad to help you learn to use *Readers' Guide to Periodical Literature*. She will also be able to tell you whether the school library has the back issues of the magazines you need.

Do not forget that the articles in many of these magazines are not really scientific articles. Rather, they are popularized versions of science, intended for the ordinary reader. Although the articles may be based on scientific work, some of the material may be glamorized or glorified; the information may be incomplete, inaccurate, or exaggerated. Therefore, if you are going to do a really serious piece of work, you will need a better source of information, such as research reports, to be considered next.

3. Original articles by research workers. These articles are by far the best and most accurate sources of information on research. They are written by the people who do the actual research. Unfortunately, they are frequently technical, and often they are written in a way which is difficult for boys and girls to understand. However, any student who takes the time to analyze and study some of these original research articles is sure to profit from them.

Where do you find these articles? Well, there are numerous scientific journals (as they are called), catering to the different fields of science. Some of these are listed below:

a. *Science* is a weekly magazine which deals with all the fields of science. It usually contains short descriptions of research projects carried out by scientists all over the United States.

b. The *Journal of Heredity*, by contrast, is a monthly magazine which restricts its articles to the subject of heredity.

c. The *Journal of Bacteriology* carries reports of investigations dealing with bacteria.

d. The *Journal of Experimental Zoology* deals with studies of animals.

e. Other noteworthy scientific publications are as follows: *Journal of Agricultural Research, American Journal of Botany, Journal of Immunology, Journal of the American Chemical Society, Proceedings of the Society for Experimental Biology and Medicine, Journal of the Proceedings of the National Academy of Science, Archives of Biochemistry, Journal of Biological Chemistry, The American Naturalist, Journal of the American Physical Society,* and the *Botanical Gazette.* Every scientific society has its journal. In addition, many colleges publish scientific magazines to report the work of their research men. Hospitals, medical associations, commercial laboratories, scientific foundations — all these have publications, too. Of course, these journals are not usually found in the high school library, but they may be available in college libraries, medical libraries, or large public libraries.

To help the reader locate articles, each journal prepares an index from time to time. The index usually lists the articles alphabetically by author and subject. Even better, there are special

journals known as "indexing journals" which do for scientific literature very much the same that the *Readers' Guide to Periodical
Literature* does for general magazine articles. For example:

a. *The International Index to Periodicals* is a subject and
author index of about 240 journals in the field of pure science and
the humanities.

b. *The Agricultural Index* covers magazines on agricultural
and related subjects such as botany, biology, and genetics.

c. In addition, there are several "abstracting journals" such
as *Biological Abstracts* and *Chemical Abstracts.* These give brief
summaries of the important articles appearing in current science
literature. By means of these summaries, abstracting journals may
help you decide which articles are appropriate for your problem.

As you can see, the total amount of science literature is over-
whelming, and no pupil can possibly keep up with it or read it all.
However, by reading *a single one* of these original science papers,
you can gain many advantages. First of all, you may find more references, because each author usually refers to others who have
worked in the same field. Second, you might learn a great deal
about the history of the subject, because the author often deals
with this. Third, you may learn something about how to set up your
own experiment. Fourth, you may see how a scientist reports his
work.

Although it may mean hard work to struggle through a scientific paper, in the long run, it is well worthwhile. When you find a
paper which you think can be exceptionally useful, you can sometimes get a copy of it for your own use by writing to the author. Tell
him why you are interested in his investigation, and ask him if a
reprint is available. Usually the author is willing to send a copy, if
he has one to spare, and if he thinks that it will be used for a worthwhile purpose.

4. Review articles. Occasionally a scientific journal will publish what is called a *review article* on some subject. Usually it is
written by one of the outstanding workers in the field, and it generally traces the history of the subject from its beginnings to the most
recent work being done. Obviously, a survey of this type is ideal
for giving you a thorough background in the subject. It gives you a
"bird's-eye view" of all the work in the field, and you can see
where your problem fits in. Furthermore, review articles usually include a large number of references; you can select those which you

want to follow up. In such magazines as *The Scientific Monthly* or *The Scientific American*, you can frequently find review articles which, while somewhat technical, are quite readable.

While review articles appear from time to time in almost every scientific magazine, there are certain journals which specialize in them. Some of these are: *Chemical Reviews, Annual Review of Biochemistry, Quarterly Review of Biology, Botanical Reviews, Biological Reviews, Physiological Reviews, Physical Reviews,* and *Bacteriological Reviews*. These review journals are probably not available in your school library, but it will repay you to take the trouble to locate some of them and try to read an article or two.

5. Other sources of information. Although there are many other sources from which you can gather information for your project, only a few will be mentioned here. First is the encyclopedia. Somehow, when boys and girls are asked to look something up, they immediately think of the encyclopedia. While a good encyclopedia is usually a reliable source of information, it is not the best place to do preliminary reading for a project. However, there is no harm in reading the encyclopedia article on the subject of your interest. It usually does give a broad view of the whole subject.

Many libraries maintain what is called a " Vertical File." This is a collection of current pamphlets, government publications, newspaper clippings, magazine articles, and other materials arranged by subject matter. If your school library maintains a " Vertical File," don't fail to take advantage of it.

Each year the federal government issues hundreds of publications of every imaginable type. Some of these describe scientific work carried on by research men in various experimental stations scattered over the country. The publications are often available at small cost from the Superintendent of Documents (U.S. Government Printing Office, Washington 25, D.C.); sometimes they may be obtained free of charge directly from your congressman.

Of course, just reading is not enough. You must digest what you read, and understand it. You must make some record of what you read, so that you can easily refer to your notes or to the source material itself. The next chapter contains some advice on recording your readings.

15 Preparatory Work— Recording the Readings

Thomas A. Edison once said, "When I want to discover something, I begin by reading up everything that has been done along that line in the past — that's what all these books in the library are for. I see what has been accomplished at great labor and expense in the past. I gather the data of many thousands of experiments as a starting point, and then I make thousands more."

It is one thing to locate and read material which deals with the project you are planning to do, but it is an altogether different matter to remember what you read, or where you read it. Perhaps the following has happened to you: you were writing a report, and you needed a certain bit of information that you remembered reading somewhere — but where? How unfortunate! You can't remember. Was it in this book? Or was it in the magazine article you read in the school library? With a sigh, you start hunting through all the books and articles which you read recently. Perhaps you find what you are looking for, and perhaps you don't. In the meantime, you have wasted a good deal of valuable time.

It is always wise to keep some sort of record of your readings. If you do so, you can "lay your hands" on each elusive bit of information, because you have it "pinned down," so to speak. Furthermore, when the time comes for you to write a report describing your project, experiment, or investigation, you will need accurate references for your bibliography. Let us consider how to keep a record of what you read. Two suggestions are given below.

1. Using a notebook. If you decide to use a notebook for recording your readings, reserve the notebook for this purpose only. Do not put anything else into the notebook. For each article you read, head a page with the name of the author, the title of the article, the date of publication, and the source (that is, the name of the magazine or book in which you found the article). Put down also the place where you found the magazine or book, so that if you should want to refer to the original article again you will know exactly where to find it.

Now, as you read the article, put down the important points. Record special methods or techniques used by the author. Write down any ideas that come to you as you read. Finally, summarize the article. Don't forget to copy any references which are listed, and which you think you may want to follow up. Naturally, the more detailed your record is, the better it will serve you later on when you want to make use of it.

2. Using a card file. Probably the most convenient way to record your readings is by means of a card file. Such a file has certain advantages. The cards can be organized in many different ways, and they can be reorganized very easily if there is reason for so doing. The file can be expanded or contracted at will. Cards can be destroyed if they are outdated, and new ones added as additional information is found. Cards are comparatively cheap to buy, and you can get them in a large variety of different colors for easy classification (as explained a little later on). File cards come in different sizes, but cards measuring 3 inches by 5 inches, or 5 inches by 7 inches, are most commonly used. The 5 x 7 size allows more space for writing, but for most matters the 3 x 5 size is satisfactory. This is the standard size file card used in libraries, and you can prepare it in the following manner to record what you have read.

HIBERNATION

BARKER, WILL — "The Big Sleep Is On."
   <u>Natural</u> <u>History</u>, Vol. 63, No. 9; Nov. 1954;
      pp. 402–405. (School library)

Describes changes during hibernation in many animals.
Also estivation.
    Woodchuck — buries self in tunnel. Breathing
      slows & almost stops. Pulse faint. Temp.
      down to 40–50°F. Insensible to touch or

(continued over)

This card reminds you that your school library has the issue of *Natural History* magazine for November, 1954, and that on pages 402–405 there is an article on hibernation written by Will Barker under the title of " The Big Sleep Is On." The card also summarizes the information which the article provides. Naturally, you do not need to restrict yourself to one side of the card, or even to a single card. You can continue adding information on the reverse side of the card and on a second card.

By using cards of several colors, you can classify different types of information for each reading. You can choose your own color scheme, provided you stick to it consistently. Just decide on a different color for each kind of information you want to keep on file. For example:

Use a *white* card for recording *facts* and *general information.*
Use a *yellow* card for recording *techniques.*
Use a *blue* card for *bibliography — books* and *articles.*
Use a *pink* card for *ideas* you want to follow up.
Use a *green* card for *historical information* and *biography.*

The sample below illustrates how a technique might be recorded on a yellow card, if you are following the pattern outlined above.

SALIVARY CHROMOSOMES

Permanent slides of giant salivary chromosomes.
Technique described in <u>DROSOPHILA GUIDE</u>, by M. Demerec
    & B. P. Kaufmann, Carnegie Inst. of Wash., 1945,
    pp. 12–30 (many illustrations)

1. Grow larvae in uncrowded conditions at low temp.
2. Use fully grown larvae (just before pupation).
3. Dissect out salivary gland in salt sol.
   (7 parts NaCl in 1000 parts distilled water)

(continued over)

As the number of completed cards begins to increase, it is best to get a box for them. If you keep them neatly organized, you will have an efficient system for recording your readings.

16 Preparatory Work — Learning Basic Techniques

While you are doing your preliminary reading, you should also be learning the basic techniques which your work will require. Once an experiment is under way it is a little late to begin learning a special technique. The time to practice is before you begin. Here are a few illustrations:

1. Suppose you are doing an experiment which involves hydroponics (growing plants without soil), and you must make up a water solution containing 3 grams of this, 0.5 grams of that, and 25 milligrams of something else. You must learn how to use a scale, preferably the analytical balance. To operate an analytical balance takes a certain amount of skill and practice, which you must develop in advance.

2. Suppose your investigation deals with protozoa. You must learn how to grow them, and how to isolate individual specimens. In order to isolate a single protozoan, you will find it convenient to have a capillary pipette, which you will have to make by yourself. Or perhaps you want to concentrate your culture so that there are many protozoa in a small quantity of fluid. To do this you will have to learn to use a centrifuge. If you think you can be successful with these things on the first attempt, you will be sadly disappointed.

3. Are you considering an investigation in the field of bacteriology? Here are a few of the techniques which you must be prepared to carry out: preparation of culture media, plating Petri dishes with the culture media, making slants and stabs, sterilization of glassware and media, rolling cotton plugs, and transfer techniques. Don't let this list frighten you. There is nothing especially difficult about any of these techniques. You can learn them easily; but you cannot do so overnight. You must prepare in advance.

4. Consider an experiment which three boys recently performed. They carried out an experiment to find the effect of vitamin B_{12} on regeneration of blood in rabbits. In order to perform the experiment, the boys had to produce anemia in their rabbits, and then inject the vitamin into the experimental group, while withholding it from the control group. Following this, they had to take periodic blood samples and compare the blood of experimental animals with that of control animals. Consider all the techniques they had to learn. How do you bleed a rabbit to make it anemic? How is the vitamin injected into the living animal? How do you take a blood sample? How do you make a blood smear once you have the sample? How do you count the blood corpuscles to see if the animals really are anemic? Fortunately for this particular group of boys, the father of one of them was a doctor. He taught them the skills *before* they began their project.

Perhaps the experiment which you select may not require many new techniques; on the other hand, perhaps it may require more new techniques than any of the examples cited. Whatever the case may be, it should be quite evident to you that practice must come before you try to apply the technique to your investigation.

One more piece of advice. Keep a record of all the techniques you learn. Describe them on file cards, and add them to your file of information, together with your sources of information. After you have practiced the technique for a while, add your own comments to the card. Did you find any special trick to make the technique more effective? Note it on the card. If you had any special difficulty using the technique, note that, too. You will soon build up a file which will serve you not only for the work you are doing at the moment, but also later on for other investigations.

Where can you learn the techniques you need? Well, perhaps there is someone who can teach you — a doctor, a parent, a teacher, a laboratory assistant, an older brother or sister. You can also learn from special books. A short list of books which may help you locate the technique you need can be found in the bibliography in the back of this book.

Still another way of learning techniques is to volunteer your services at a hospital or commercial laboratory. If you are accepted at one of these places, you may be asked to wash test tubes, or sweep the floors, but at the same time you will have the opportunity of watching experts at work.

17 Planning the Investigation

Once you have done your preliminary reading and learned your fundamental techniques, it is time to pause and take stock. You are not yet ready to plunge into the investigation. You need to do *your detailed planning.*

A thorough plan is really important. A little time spent on preparing a proper plan at this stage may very well save you a great deal of time — and many headaches — later on. You will protect yourself against that ever-present possibility of forgetting to do something. By planning thoroughly at the beginning, you may avoid having to say later, when it is too late, " Why didn't I think of that before? " So take plenty of time in drawing up your plan of action. Get all the advice you can. Discuss it with your adviser, your teacher, your brother. Think it through thoroughly, and then prepare a tentative plan in writing. Submit this plan to your adviser and ask him to criticize it for you.

What should be in this tentative plan? The outline which follows suggests ten things for you to consider. If you follow this outline, you are pretty certain to include in your tentative plan all the information which your adviser will need to understand what you want to do. He will be able to guide you accordingly.

1. What is the problem?   Here you should have a clear, concise statement of your problem, and a paragraph outlining its scope. You might, if you like, include the relevant historical background which explains why you selected this particular problem.

2. What do you plan to do to solve the problem?   This section of your outline should be one or more paragraphs telling precisely how you plan to proceed. Be sure to state whether you are planning a series of observations, a trial-and-error procedure, a planned experiment, a library research program, or whatever else it may be. Then describe it as exactly as you can. If a diagram will clarify the setup you plan to use, include the diagram in your outline.

3. What equipment, apparatus, and/or materials will you need? List here any special needs which will arise during your investigation. Will it require plants, animals, special chemicals, or unusual apparatus? If so, list them, and state how and where you expect to get them. Tell also how you intend to take care of them. If living things are involved in your experiment, indicate what plants or animals you are going to use, and explain why you selected these particular organisms as the subject of your investigation. The importance of choosing the right materials for an experiment was pointed out by Gregor Mendel * in 1865 when he wrote, " The value and utility of any experiment are determined by the fitness of the material to the purpose for which it is used. . . ."

4. What information will you need? In this section, explain what observations you plan to make, and what data you intend to collect. Tell also in what form you intend to record the information which you will collect.

5. What preparations have you made? Here, tell your adviser what you have read on the subject of your experiment, to what authorities you have referred, what techniques you have learned, and anything else which will help him decide whether you are really ready to begin work.

6. What do you plan to do with the information which you collect? Write one or more paragraphs explaining to your adviser how you plan to analyze or interpret the data, and how you will use the data to reach a conclusion. If you think the results might come out in one of several different ways, tell what conclusion you could reach in each case.

7. How long will the investigation take? Give your adviser some estimate of the time you think you will need to carry out the entire proposed plan. If possible, suggest the date when you would like to begin, and when you hope to complete the job. Do not overlook the fact that school holidays may interfere.

---

* Gregor Johann Mendel (1822–1844) was an Austrian botanist who discovered certain principles of heredity relating to the transfer of dominant and recessive physical traits from parents to offspring.

8. Where do you propose to carry out the investigation? Do you plan to work in the school's project room, at home, or in some laboratory? Is your home properly equipped for the kind of thing you are planning to do? Who will supervise your work?

9. What value or importance does your proposed investigation have? Explain here how your investigation fits into the broader picture of general research in the field. Also point out any practical applications which may arise from what you are doing. Remember, however, it is not essential that you do an experiment for its practical applications. Many discoveries in pure science have no apparent use. Often, many years later, a use is found for what was originally considered a useless discovery. This idea was expressed very well by Eric Hodgins in the April, 1955, issue of *Fortune* magazine when he said:

> The temptation in this country is almost overwhelming to justify every human activity in terms of its immediate usefulness or efficiency. But the yardstick of instant usefulness does not properly measure research. Most great thoughts, most basic observations, begin by being "useless." The Newtonian physics once belonged in this category. So did the Mendelian laws of heredity. So did the Bohr atom. So did quantum mechanics. So did the equivalence of mass and energy.

Don't give up your idea because you cannot foresee any practical applications. However, if there are obvious applications, state what they are.

10. What weaknesses does your proposed plan have? Here is a good place to criticize your own plan. It may have several weak points or limitations. You should be aware of these before you begin work. Of course, if you find too many faults in your own proposed plan, perhaps it might be worth your while to look for a better plan. In all probability, no single plan will ever include all the items just listed. However, the more complete and thorough your plan is, the more useful it will be to you and to your adviser. It is surprising how often something seemingly insignificant may make an investigation go wrong. Don't take any chances. Prepare as careful a plan as possible, and leave ample space for your adviser's comments.

Keep in mind the necessity of careful planning as you read the sample plan which is given in the next chapter.

18 A Sample Plan for an Investigation

In the previous chapter the importance of adequate planning was stressed, and it was pointed out that — at the very least — a good plan must answer the following questions:

1. What is the problem?
2. What do you plan to do to solve the problem?
3. What equipment, apparatus, and/or materials will you need?
4. What information will you need?
5. What preparations have you made?
6. What do you plan to do with the information which you collect?
7. How long will the investigation take?
8. Where do you propose to carry out the investigation?
9. What value or importance does your proposed investigation have?
10. What weaknesses does your proposed plan have?

Perhaps it would help you in making your own plan if you saw what a typical student plan for a project looks like. For this reason, a sample plan is given on the next two pages, exactly as it was presented to the adviser. You will note that the adviser has raised certain questions about some of the statements in the plan. As you read the plan, see if it answers the ten questions that are outlined above; and see if you can answer the questions raised by the adviser.

As you will see, a good plan gives your adviser a clear picture of what you are planning to do, so that he can criticize intelligently. Of course no amount of criticism written in the margins of your plan can substitute for a personal meeting with your adviser. If possible, try to discuss your plan with him personally as soon as you have digested his written criticisms.

A good plan! Please read my comments, and make the few necessary corrections. When can you come in to see me with the corrected plan?

Tentative <u>Plan</u> <u>for</u> <u>a</u> <u>Project</u>

Submitted to Mr. ————

On Feb. ——, 19——

by J———— G————

I know that adding fertilizers to the lawn or the garden makes the plants grow better. My father also uses some fertilizer dissolved in water for his house plants. But it seems to me that a good deal of the fertilizer is wasted when you put it into the soil, because the plants never get it.

How will you state the problem?

This led me to wonder whether it is better to inject the fertilizer right into the plant than to put the fertilizer into the ground. I would like to test this by performing the following experiment. I will use 6 onions planted in flowerpots. To 3 of the pots I will add

How much?

a certain amount of soluble fertilizer to the soil once a week. In the other 3 pots I will inject the same amount of the same fertilizer directly into the onion once a week.

How do you plan to make up the solution?

To do this I will need a hypodermic and some soluble fertilizer. My uncle who is a doctor loaned me the hypodermic and showed me how to use it. And my father has some <u>Rapid-Gro</u>, which is a soluble fertilizer that you can buy in any garden supply store. I have already practiced using the hypodermic to inject liquids into plants. I tried bean plants and coleus, but the stems are too thin, and they break when I push the needle in.

Good idea

My father suggested that I use onions, which will give me plenty of room to inject.

Your hypothesis?

I think that the injected onions will grow bigger and faster than the uninjected onions because the fertilizer is put right inside where the cells can get

Good!

to it. But I will have to wait until I see the results.

I will want to see whether the injected onions sprout faster than the
uninjected onions and whether the plants
grow faster and bigger. I will record
the date when I plant the onions, and
each time I give them fertilizer. Then I
will note the date when green leaves
first begin to come out. After the
onions have sprouted, I will keep a daily
record in which I will note the number of
leaves, and the height of the tallest
leaf of each onion. I will also watch to
see if there is any difference in color.

If I see that the injected onions
sprout faster and taller than the controls, I will conclude that injecting is
a better way to give fertilizers to
plants. If there is no difference between the two, then my conclusion will be
that either way of giving fertilizer is
just as good. And lastly, if the uninjected plants do better, I will conclude
that the injection in some way harms the
plant.

I think I can finish this experiment
in about 4 or 5 weeks. I'd like to grow
the onions in the utility room of my
house because it is still too cold to
plant them outside. I have a table for
the plants and there is a window for
light. I'll keep turning the plants
each day so they won't grow one-sided.

I read a great deal about fertilizers and plants, but I couldn't find anything about injecting fertilizers into
plants. Maybe this experiment has never
been done before. But if it works, maybe
it will be useful in growing plants.

19 Carrying Out the Investigation

By this time you are well on the road to a successful piece of research. It has been a long process — planning, discussing, reading, practicing — but at last the day of days has arrived! You are ready to set up and go!

But wait a minute. Don't be impatient. You have spent so much time getting ready for this moment that it would be a pity to spoil everything now. It is always a good idea to "make haste slowly," so let us stop for a minute and review.

What have you done so far? You should have selected a problem, analyzed it, studied it, and discussed it many times with other people. You should have a clear picture of *what* you want to do. You should have gone to the library to read about it, practiced necessary techniques until you can do them skillfully, and decided how to set up your experiment. You should know precisely what you are going to look for. You should know exactly *how* you are going about your work. If you know or have done all these things, you are really ready to set up your project or experiment.

You must see to it that you have all your materials and equipment at hand. This should be obvious enough, because without these things you cannot do what you have planned. It can be pretty embarrassing to get caught short. Suppose, according to plan, your rabbit is to get an injection at exactly 2:00 P.M. on October 23. You get all set, and suddenly at 1:59 P.M. you discover that you don't have enough of the drug which is supposed to be injected. Too bad! All your fine planning is wasted as the result of a careless oversight.

You already have a clear picture of your plan of action, but reread your final plan anyway. Reread it several times so that it becomes a part of you; so that you cannot forget the correct sequence of steps in your investigation. Review in your mind the several possible ways in which your experiment or investigation can turn out, and how you will recognize each of them. Think for a moment of the errors which can creep in, and how you can avoid them.

You must prepare the notebook or logbook in which you will keep the records of your experiment. Set up in advance the tables, charts, or graphs which you will need to determine the outcome of the experiment. Suggestions for how to keep your records will be found in the next chapter.

Now take a deep breath, cross your fingers very unscientifically, and get started. Set up your experiment — and good luck to you. Don't expect miracles. Things may not work out quite the way you planned. This happens even to famous scientists in famous laboratories. Dr. Charles F. Kettering* once put it this way: " Set the thing up, and there isn't one chance in a thousand that the thing will work the way you expect it to. But it won't fail the way you expect it to, either. That is the way you learn."

Keep your mind alert and your eyes wide open. Don't allow yourself to be blinded by what you think *should* happen. You may see something which you did not expect, in addition to that which you are seeking. Don't overlook something because it seems unimportant at the moment. You can never tell in advance which detail will turn out to be the most important one. Don't focus your attention so strongly on one thing that you overlook everything else that happens. Here is an actual case which illustrates this last point:

A certain boy was carrying on a diet experiment in which he expected his experimental rats to lose weight. He checked weights carefully each day, until one day his younger brother suddenly remarked as he watched, " What's the matter with that rat? Why is he limping? " Then for the first time the experimenter became conscious of the fact that his experimental animals had something wrong with their legs. He had concentrated so hard on weight loss that he had overlooked a very obvious result of the poor diet — a crippling effect on the joints.

If for some reason you need to modify your experiment, remember this bit of advice given by Professor W. I. B. Beveridge: " Vary one thing at a time, and make a note of all you do." ** He means that it is wise to make only one change in your experiment at a time. And above all, write it down. Don't depend on memory.

---

* Dr. Charles F. Kettering is a director of the Sloan-Kettering Institute for Cancer Research.
** Professor W. I. B. Beveridge, *Art of Scientific Investigation*, Norton, 1950.

20 Recording the Observations

"Make a note of all you do!" This is a wonderful bit of advice for anyone setting out to do a research project, but it only goes half way. To be complete the advice should read, "Make a note of all you do, *and all you observe.*"

There are many reasons for keeping exact records. Perhaps the most important of these is the fact that you can never tell at the moment of observation whether something will or will not be important when you are ready to draw a conclusion. It is better to make extensive notes, eliminating some of the unnecessary details later, than to record only the high lights and regret it when you find you don't remember just the one detail which can make or break your experiment. In scientific work there is no such thing as an unimportant occurrence. Everything that happens is important. Make a note of all you do and all you observe!

By studying the records of some of our outstanding scientists we can gain some understanding of how they carried on their experimental research work. Take Edison, for example. He left us about 2,500 notebooks in which he recorded his experiments. These were pocket-sized notebooks, to fit into the pocket of a laboratory work coat. Each notebook contains 250–300 pages packed full of information, data, diagrams, questions to be answered, ideas to be followed up, instructions to his assistants, and some doodling. These notebooks are now preserved in a special vault in Edison's laboratory at West Orange, New Jersey. An extract from one of his notebooks is reproduced as Figure 11.

FIGURE 11. *A selection from the notebooks of Thomas A. Edison. Why are records so important to scientists?*

Black Autographic Ink

No 1

Tried lampblack and castor oil alone ground well
in a mortar, it work exceedingly well.
Tried Glycerine and lampblack, don't work well
There seems to be an antagnism between the two
so that even a mechanical mixture seems almost
impossible, the lampblack settles out. by rubbing
the roller a great number of times over the stencil
paper the ink assumes a very pale look, but if
the finger is rubbed over it a dense black streak
is seen. another phenomenon is noticed, the blue
ruled lines upon the paper appear to repel the ink
and show quite white   the mechanical mixture
of lampblack with castor oil is so perfect that
one would believe that it was soluable, though
it is almost certain that it isn't.
The Castor oil - lampblack ink does not appear
to blot through the paper enough to prevent the
taking of a large number of copies,   By placing
Castor oil, Olive Oil, Cod liver oil, Lard oil
and Glycerine upon paper, the Olive oil came
through first the Castor oil 4th and the glycerine
did not come through for some time, the
glycerine used was crude and quite thick
though not any thicker than the castor oil
Common printing ink thinned with castor oil
works perfectly, and if the printers ink is
cheap enough leaves nothing more to be
desired, Common printers ink does not mix
at all with glycerine, at least there is an
exceedingly poor mechanical mixture,
Powdered proto Fe and nutgalls put
together and ground with glycerine gives
a fair ink but has not a sufficient depth
of color to be satisfactory, The most
perfect and conspicuous copies ever taken on the
Autographic press were taken this evening with ink
formed of printers ink thinned by castor oil and
ground in a mortar some two weeks previously.
   October 3 1875   Thos A Edison
          Chas Batchelor James Adams

Of course, your records will not require 2,500 notebooks, but you certainly should have one. In it you should keep an up-to-date and accurate record of everything you do, and everything you observe with regard to your investigation. One good way of doing this is by keeping a logbook, like the record which the captain of a ship must keep for every voyage. In his logbook, the captain records every event of the day such as how much distance the ship covered, weather and wind conditions, and any special occurrences either on the ship or on the ocean around. Here are a few suggestions concerning your entries in your "log."

1. Dating your entries. Every entry should be dated. Whether you make an entry every day or only once a week will depend on your particular investigation. There is no set time interval at which entries must be made. In some cases entries will be needed every twenty minutes, while in others, one entry a week will be sufficient. Always put down the date, and the time, too, if it is necessary.

2. The final plan of your experiment. After you and your adviser have agreed on the final plan of your experiment, this plan should be permanently recorded in your "log" for easy reference.

3. Description of the setting up of the experiment. Give a detailed account of what you did in setting up your investigation. Be sure to give the date when your experiment began.

4. Day by day (or week by week) description of everything that you do and everything which happens with reference to your experiment. Record all data immediately, while things are in front of your eyes, and details are fresh in your mind. Do not delude yourself with the idea that you can record important details later. Even a few minutes later may be too late.

5. Ideas and questions which occur to you. While you are working, an idea may suddenly pop into your head. Even if you cannot see any direct use for the idea at the moment, write it down. You may find that it takes on importance later. Various questions may also occur to you. Some of these may be side issues to your investigations; others may be entirely unrelated. Perhaps some of them may be worth following up at a later date in another investigation.

6. Weak links in your experiment. You may now realize that your plan has certain weaknesses which you did not recognize before. If you repeat this experiment, you will want to remedy these weaknesses. Record them. When you report your results, you will want to point them out as limitations.

7. Criticisms of techniques which you are using. If you find that certain techniques are not satisfactory, make notes of the reasons. If you find a way to overcome a limitation in a technique, write that down, too. You will need this information for your report.

8. Charts and tables of data. You may find it convenient to tabulate the observed data in some sort of chart. Choose that form of chart which is convenient for the type of data you are collecting. Information about charts and tables is given in the next chapter.

9. Pictures and photographs of your materials. It is an old maxim that one picture is worth a thousand words. Often a drawing of a specimen to show a specific change which has occurred is far superior to a word picture of the change. An actual photograph may be even better. Remember, though, that a picture without some kind of explanation is easily misunderstood. For each picture, write a brief description which points up the important things to be seen.

No doubt other ideas which should go into the " log " will occur to you as you proceed with your work. *Write down at once whatever occurs to you.*

Some parts of an actual student log are reproduced below. In this case, entries in the " log " itself were made only for special events or special observations. Routine, daily measurements were recorded directly in tables which were prepared in advance. One of the tables is also reproduced as an illustration.

```
3/13/54    Today I prepared the fertilizers as follows:

           1 teaspoonful Vigoro to 1 quart water
           1 teaspoonful Rapid-Gro to 1 quart water

           Solutions stirred, filtered through cotton, and
           stored in quart milk bottles.

           Sprouted onions are not all equal in number and
           size of leaves.  One has 7 leaves with the tall-
           est leaf 7 inches tall.  Another has 6 leaves,
           with the tallest 2 inches.  The third has 5
           leaves with tallest 2 inches.

           I decided to use the best-developed plant as
           control.  Reason -- if a smaller plant injected
           with fertilizer can shoot up and overtake the
```

larger control, it will be clearer proof of the effect of fertilizers.

Injections will be made tonight, and every Saturday night after this. This will be marked on table by an arrow. One cc. of <u>Vigoro</u> solution or <u>Rapid-Gro</u> solution will be used. Control will be stuck with needle, but no injection will be made.

Measurements will be taken daily and recorded in table marked Expt. No. 1.
(1) Height of tallest leaf in inches.
(2) Number of leaves.

3/16/54   Changed water in all the cups.
Noticed that <u>Rapid-Gro</u> plant has the best root system. <u>Vigoro</u> plant has next best. Control plant has very small root system compared with the other two.

3/18/54   Both injected onions growing faster and taller than control. Is this due to fertilizer or <u>water which was injected</u>? <u>Should be tested</u>!

3/20/54   Second injection in Expt. No. 1.
Began Expt. No. 2. New set of 3 onions.
These onions <u>not</u> sprouted. Also, in this experiment control will be injected with water rather than just jabbed with needle. This will tell me whether the water alone stimulates the faster growth.

The 3 new onions were injected, and set over cups of water as before. Measurements will be recorded in table marked No. 2 when growth begins.

3/26/54   In Expt. No. 2 <u>Rapid-Gro</u> plant shows first sign of growth. Expt. No. 1 continues — see table.

3/27/54   <u>Vigoro</u> plant of Expt. No. 2 has now sprouted. It is about ½ inch shorter than <u>Rapid-Gro</u> plant which began sprouting yesterday.
Control plant shows no sign of leaves as yet.
Changed water in all cups.
Injected all plants according to plan.

3/29/54   Control of Expt. No. 2 has sprouted.
It is about 6 inches shorter than <u>Rapid-Gro</u> plant of this experiment. Interesting observation — fertilizers injected seemed to speed the sprouting time.
Start taking daily measurements tomorrow.

EXPERIMENT NO. 1

1954	CONTROL		VIGORO		RAPID-GRO		Inject
	Tallest Leaf	No. of Leaves	Tallest Leaf	No. of Leaves	Tallest Leaf	No. of Leaves	
3/13	4 in.	7	2 in.	6	2 in.	5	←
3/14	4¾	7	2½	8	3½	12	
3/15	5½	7	3½	11	5	13	
3/16	6⅜	8	5	12	6	14	
3/17	7	8	6½	13	7½	16	
3/18	7¾	8	7¾	13	8¾	17	
3/19	8⅜	8	9	14	10	18	
3/20	9	9	10	15	11	18	←
3/21	9½	9	11	16	12	19	
3/22	9¾	9	12	16	12¼	20	
3/23	10	9	12¾	16	14	21	
3/24	10¼	9	13¼	16	15	22	
3/25	10½	9	13½	16	15½	22	
3/26	11	9	14¾	17	16½	22	
3/27	11¼	9	15½	17	16¾	22	←
3/28	11½	9	16	17	17¼	22	
3/29	11½	9	16⅜	17	17¾	22	
3/30	11¾	9	17	17	18	22	
3/31	12	9	17¼	17	18¼	22	
4/1	12¼	9	17½	17	18½	22	
4/2	12¼	9	18	17	19	22	
4/3	12½	9	18½	17	19	22	←
4/4	13	9	19¾	17	19½	22	
4/5	‚13½	9	19¾	17	19½	22	
4/6	14	9	20½	17	19¾	22	
4/7	14½	9	20½	17	20½	22	

3/30/54	First measurements taken in onions of Expt. No. 2. Recorded in table marked Expt. No. 2. [table deleted]
4/3/54	Since the injected onions seem to be growing larger and faster than the uninjected controls, it occurred to me that this idea might be put to practical use. How can it be tested?
4/10/54	Discussed the idea with my father. He suggested that I try it on some gladiolus bulbs and some onion sets which he intends to plant later this month. I think I will.
4/18/54	Prepared plot for the glads and onion sets. Used 30 glads and 24 onion sets divided into 3 groups, each consisting of 10 glads and 8 onion sets. This will be called Expt. No. 3. Each bulb in Vigoro group injected with 1 cc. Vigoro solution. Each bulb in Rapid-Gro group injected with 1 cc. Rapid-Gro solution. Each bulb in control group injected with 1 cc. water. These will be planted as in diagram [below].

●●●●●●●●●●	●●●●●●●●●●	●●●●●●●●●●	⊕⊕⊕⊕	● Gladiolus
Vigoro	Rapid-Gro	Control	Old Onions	★ Onion Set
★★★★★★★★	★★★★★★★★	★★★★★★★★	⊕⊕⊕⊕	⊕ Old Onion

The onions which were growing indoors (Expt. No. 1 and No. 2) were transplanted outdoors. I want to see if there is any difference in date of flowering.

Would you like to know how this experiment turns out? Well, why don't you try it yourself sometime? If it's worth knowing about, it's worth trying. Your "log" of your experiment or investigation may stimulate someone else to work on the same problem.

A chapter on recording your observations could not possibly be complete without some remarks about accuracy. Everybody agrees that accuracy of observation is basic to the formulation of valid conclusions. Here are a few suggestions to keep in mind.

1. Try to use objective measurements whenever possible. Suppose you record in your "log" that plant A is bigger than plant B, what does it mean? Does "bigger" mean taller, thicker, heavier, more leaves, or what? Wouldn't it be better to say, "Plant A is 36 centimeters tall, while plant B is only 30 centimeters tall"? The second statement is obviously better, because it gives exact and objective measurements of both plants. So use measuring instruments — scales, micrometers, colorimeters, quantitative tests — and record the exact figures.

2. Describe clearly what you are measuring. Imagine two people measuring the same cat. One measures from top of head to base of tail. The other measures from tip of ear to tip of tail. Which one is correct? Actually both are correct, since they both measured the cat. Yet the two measurements will not coincide. Therefore, be sure to record the limits of your measurements — from what point to what other point — so that a person repeating your experiment or checking your results will measure in exactly the same way.

3. Check your apparatus frequently. There is always the danger that your measuring devices may go out of adjustment. If this should happen, and you do not notice it immediately, a whole series of measurements may be off, and therefore your results will be unreliable or incorrect.

4. Make sure you know how to use the equipment. Even the finest measuring instrument will give incorrect measurements if it is used improperly. So make sure you know exactly how to use the instrument and how to read the measurements it gives.

5. Use the instrument which is appropriate to the thing you want to measure. For example, would you use a 12-inch ruler to lay off 100 yards on an outdoor track? This would be rather foolish, wouldn't it? It would be much easier, and more accurate too, if you used a long steel tape measure. The 12-inch ruler just isn't the correct instrument for the job. Neither is the ruler the correct measuring device for determining the size of a paramecium, nor an analytical balance the correct instrument for weighing out a pound of butter, nor the milliammeter the correct device for measuring current supplying 30 amperes. You must be careful that you choose a measuring tool which is appropriate for what you are measuring.

6. Check your measurements carefully. Don't be satisfied with the first weighing or the first reading on a meter. Even experts make mistakes. If possible, check every measurement before you accept it. Perhaps you can check it by a different method.

7. Know the limits of accuracy of your measurements. What does it mean when we say that the distance from the earth to the sun is 93,000,000 miles? Certainly it does *not* mean that the distance is exactly 93,000,000 miles. Rather, it is an approximation. It means that we believe the distance between earth and sun to be *no less than 92,500,000 miles and no more than 93,500,000 miles* — somewhere around 93,000,000 miles. It is obvious that the six zeroes are *not* really significant, since the measurement is correct only within the limits of a possible error of 500,000 miles.

Similarly, when we say we live one quarter of a mile from school, we mean approximately one quarter of a mile. It could be a little more or a little less. However, when a surveyor measures off one quarter of a mile for a track meet, he must be much more accurate. He may say that he has measured the track to be .25000 of a mile in length. Notice that he writes three zeros after the .25. This means that the track is no shorter than .24995 of a mile and no longer than .25005 of a mile. He is guaranteeing an error no greater than 5/100,000 of a mile one way or the other. In this case the zeros *are* significant, and we say that the surveyor's measurement has five significant figures.

This leads us to the question of recording observations. To how many decimal places should the work be carried? Naturally, this will depend on the problem on which you are working. It also depends on the accuracy of your measuring instruments, and the point at which you are forced to estimate.

Suppose you are using a meter stick which is marked off in centimeters. You measure an object, and find that it measures 14 cm. (centimeters), with a little left over. You estimate that the amount left over is a little less than half a centimeter, so you put the measurement down as 14.4 cm. You are sure about the 14 cm., and you have estimated the .4 cm. Can you estimate accurately any further than this? Can you say that the extra bit is .45 or .46 cm.? Probably not. We will assume that 14.4 cm. is as close as you can come with the measuring instrument at hand. So you record your observation with three significant figures as 14.4 cm.

Now suppose we get a better ruler. Suppose we get one which is marked in millimeters. We can now carry our measurement to one more significant figure, if we want to. We can now say our object is 144.6 mm. long, or 14.46 cm. long. Again we have estimated the last place, but all the other figures are accurately read from the ruler. If we use a micrometer, we may even go further.

Still, how far do we want to go? This is where good judgment comes in. For each problem we must determine how fine our measurements can be, considering the precision of our technique and the accuracy of our measuring devices. As a rule, never try to estimate more than one place beyond what your instrument measures accurately. If you have calculations to make, based upon your measurements, do not carry into your calculations more decimal places than are found in your crudest measurements.

8. Describe clearly your subjective measurements. Suppose in your experiment that you must distinguish different degrees of greenness in plants. You may have to set up a scale of greenness against which to compare your plants. It would be somewhat like the scale of redness which a doctor reads when he wants to determine the amount of hemoglobin in the blood of a patient. Do not forget to attach your scale of greenness to your report, so that those who read your report can tell what your measures of greenness really mean.

In some cases subjective judgments must be made by a panel of judges, as in judging taste or flavor. If you must use this technique, be cautious. Remember that judges can easily be biased unconsciously by what they know, or by the order in which the samples are presented. If, for example, they know that you expect the experimentals to taste better than the controls, they might unconsciously decide in favor of the former if they are able to distinguish between the two groups. So you must work out a scheme of presentation which overcomes this difficulty. Don't tell the judges anything in advance except what quality you want them to judge.

9. Be intellectually honest. It is very easy to record in your observations only that which you want to see, leaving out those things which are counter to your own hypothesis. Don't do it! Don't let your own hopes and expectations bias your observations and records. Remember, it is often the unexpected observation which leads to discovery! Don't fail to record anything!

The importance of keeping complete and accurate notes was expressed in 1822 by Michael Faraday, the famous English scientist whose discoveries led to the use of modern electric generators. He wrote in the preface to one of his notebooks: " I already owe much to these notes and think such a collection worth the making by every scientific man. I am sure none would think the trouble lost after a year's experience."

21 Preparing Tables and Diagrams

In recording experimental data it is often convenient to make a table which brings together in one place all data of a certain kind. It is easier to compare things assembled on a single page than to compare the same data scattered throughout your "log."

Preparing a table is easy enough, but it does take a bit of advance planning and thinking. When you plan your experiment you decide what data you want to collect. Then you must decide in what form to record this material so that it will be easiest to grasp. Two kinds of tables or charts have already been illustrated in the sample "log" given in Chapter 20. With a little experience, you will be able to decide easily what kind of table or chart best suits your data. You will then design your own tables and charts.

Suppose you are determining the composition of a sample of sea water. You merely list all the elements for whose presence you want to test the sea water, and the amount of each element found during your analysis, as, for example, in Figure 12.

Naturally, when you write the report, you may want to reorganize the table. Maybe you will want to present the elements in the order of their quantity in sea water. However, since you do not know the correct order in advance, your rough table can be in any order, as long as you record the correct figure next to the correct element, as soon as you determine the figure.

Suppose, however, you know the figures given by reputable authorities for the composition of sea water. You want to see if sea water in different parts of the world has the same composition. You have samples from five widely scattered places. Now your table will need several columns as in Figure 13.

As you analyze each sample of sea water, you fill in the data in the table. Then you are ready to make whatever comparison you wish. Differences and similarities become evident at a glance.

FIGURE **12.** *Composition of Sea Water (Sample Taken at Long Beach, N.Y. – 10/15/56)*

ELEMENT	AMOUNT OF EACH ELEMENT *(in parts per million parts of sea water)*
Calcium	400
Carbon	30
Chlorine	19,000
Fluorine	2
Magnesium	1,300
Potassium	400
Sodium	10,000
Sulfur	900
etc.	

FIGURE **13.** *Comparison of the Composition of Samples of Sea Water from Various Sources*

ELEMENT	AMOUNT OF EACH ELEMENT *(in parts per million parts of sea water)*					
	Standard	*Atlantic Ocean (Coney Island, N.Y.)*	*Pacific Ocean (Santa Monica, Calif.)*	*Greenland Sea (Spitsbergen, Norway)*	*Mediterranean Sea (Gibraltar)*	*Indian Ocean (Colombo, Ceylon)*
Chlorine	18,980					
Sodium	10,561					
Magnesium	1,272					
Sulfur	884					
etc.						

FIGURE **14.** *Comparison of Solutions to Rectangular Block Puzzle*

SUBJECT	TIME IN SECONDS	METHOD USED BY SUBJECT
1	368	Trial and error. He started immediately to put pieces together. Ultimately found right combination.
2	241	Insight. Did nothing at first except study the pieces. Then apparently figured it out and put them together.

etc.

Sometimes comments or remarks are appropriate for items in the table. You can leave room for such remarks by arranging your table properly. Suppose you are studying the ability of human subjects to solve a problem which requires putting together certain pieces of wood to form a figure. You are interested in how long it takes the subject to solve the problem, but you also want to gain an insight into the method of approach to the problem. Perhaps your table will look like Figure 14.

A common type of table is known as the *frequency distribution*. This type of table tells how many members of a given group fall into a certain classification. For example, suppose you are studying the intelligence of a group of children, and you have just given an intelligence test. You want to summarize the I.Q. ratings of the group. First of all, you decide on certain classifications — let us say groups of ten I.Q. points. Thus, everybody who makes an I.Q. score of 90 up to but not including 100 is to be in one group, while those who get a score of 100 up to but not including 110 go into the next group. Now you list the various classes, and as you calculate an I.Q., you put a stroke next to the appropriate class. When you have four strokes, you indicate the fifth one by placing a stroke diagonally across the other four. This makes it simpler to total the frequency marks. The completed table would look somewhat like Figure 15.

Notice that a title for a table must be complete, even if it means that it will be lengthy. Now suppose you give a second I.Q. test, and you want to know whether the same people who did well on the first test also did well on the second. In other words, you want to know if both I.Q. tests measured the same thing. Your chart would now look a little different. You would need a chart of the kind known as a *scatter diagram*. Along one side of a piece of graph paper you would put the scores on the first test, while along the other side you would put the scores on the second test. When you have both scores for a certain child, you would put a dot or a stroke in the appropriate box. The completed scatter diagram would look like Figure 16.

Notice again that the title is complete; note also that the two tests do seem to measure the same thing. Students who scored low on one test scored low on the other.

Suppose you are doing a nutrition experiment in which you want to compare the growth rate of young rats on two different diets. Suppose further that you have ten rats, divided into two

FIGURE **15.** *Frequency Table of Scores for 136 Seventh Grade Students on _____ Intelligence Test, Administered March, 1957*

I.Q. CLASS-INTERVALS	TALLIES	FREQUENCY
160–169.9	|	1
150–159.9	||||/	5
140–149.9	||||/ ||||	9
130–139.9	||||/ ||||/ |||	13
120–129.9	||||/ ||||/ ||||/ ||||/ ||||/ |	26
110–119.9	||||/ ||||/ ||||/ ||||/ ||||/ ||||/ ||||/ ||||/ ||||/	45
100–109.9	||||/ ||||/ ||||/ ||||/ ||||/ ||	27
90– 99.9	||||/ ||||	9
80– 89.9	|	1
	TOTAL	136

FIGURE **16.** *Scatter Diagram Showing Correlation of Scores for 136 Seventh Graders on Two Forms of _____ Intelligence Test, Administered March, 1957*

2nd \ 1st	80–89.9	90–99.9	100–109.9	110–119.9	120–129.9	130–139.9	140–149.9	150–159.9	160–169.9	TOTAL
160–169.9									|	1
150–159.9							|||	||		5
140–149.9						||||	||||	|		9
130–139.9					|||	||||/ ||||	|			13
120–129.9				||||/ ||	|||| ||||/ ||||/	||||	|			26
110–119.9			||	||||/ ||||/ ||||/ ||||/ ||||/ ||||/ |	||||/ ||||/	||				45
100–109.9			||||/ ||||/ ||||/ ||	||||/ |||	||					27
90– 99.9		||||/	|||	|						9
80– 89.9		|								1
TOTAL	0	6	22	47	29	19	9	3	1	136

groups of five each, and that you weigh each rat daily. You might prepare a table which looks like Figure 17, and in the table record the correct figure as you weigh each animal.

FIGURE **17.** *Growth Comparison of Rats Fed a Normal Diet with Rats Fed a Diet Supplemented by* _____

DATE OF WEIGHING	WEIGHT IN GRAMS											
	CONTROL GROUP (*normal diet*)						EXPERIMENTAL GROUP (*supplemented diet*)					
	1	2	3	4	5	*Mean*	6	7	8	9	10	*Mean*
Feb. 10	48	51	50	49	53	50.2	52	48	53	49	52	50.8
11												
etc.												

Figure 18 is another example of a chart, showing in this instance the time intervals at which something is happening. The study concerns the effect of minute quantities of a certain vitamin on the population in a protozoa culture. Suppose you add one milligram of the vitamin to the culture every week. You observe that the number of protozoa in the culture rises and falls. But it is only after you make such a chart as Figure 18 that you become aware of a relationship. You notice that exactly two days after each addition of the vitamin, the population reaches a peak, and then drops again.

FIGURE **18.** *The Effect of Vitamin* _____ (*1 milligram weekly*) *added to culture of* _____

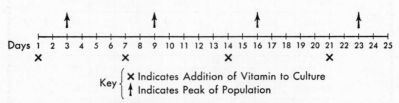

As you see, tables come in all sizes and shapes, and they can serve a multitude of purposes. You should get acquainted with tables, and learn how to use them. You will find that they are invaluable helps in any investigation.

22 Preparing Graphs, Photographs, and Drawings

How often have you heard somebody say, "One picture is worth a thousand words!" While you may not be willing to agree with this in one hundred per cent of the cases, there is no doubt that pictures can do things words alone cannot. Pictures have an attraction and an effectiveness which make people sit up and take notice. Think of the popularity of picture newspapers and picture magazines, and of the effective use of pictures in advertising to sell a product or an idea. Is there any reason why you cannot apply the same basic principles to your report to make it more attractive and effective? After all, you do want people to read your report, and you do want to get across an idea. If graphs, photographs, and drawings will help you do so, by all means use them. In a scientific report, illustrations can serve many purposes, such as the following:

1. Graphs, photographs, and drawings can save you many, many words. For example, one photograph or drawing showing how you set up the apparatus for your experiment may be better than several pages of written description. In certain fields of investigation, it is impossible to record your observations without drawings. For example, consider the field of anatomy. No amount of descriptive writing can replace a single good drawing of, say, the human digestive system.

2. Illustrations drive home an idea very forcibly. They dramatize the idea or the fact which you want to present in a way which words alone can never do. For example, it is one thing to say that rats on a vitamin D deficient diet develop rickets, and other rats on a complete diet stay healthy. But it is far more effective to show a photograph of a miserable, lethargic, bowlegged rat suffering from rickets, standing next to a healthy-looking, lively, normal rat. Such a photograph with an appropriate title says dramatically what no amount of writing can say.

3. A photograph or other illustrative record may provide a permanent record of some event which occurs only for a moment. If you present such photographic records in your report, they can be checked by others, and in this way your observations may be verified even by people who were not present when the events took place.

4. On certain charts or graphs, you can make actual measurements which are important in your report. For example, if you are studying earthquakes, and you use a seismograph to record the shocks, the tracing recorded by the seismograph can be reproduced in your report. On this tracing, you can indicate measurements which determine the severity of the shock.

If you use illustrations in your report, you must be sure that they are good illustrations. Poor illustrations may be worse than none at all. Here are a few things to consider in deciding what makes a good illustration for a scientific paper.

1. Every illustration should be *functional*. This means that it must play a useful role in your report. It is not just a decoration; it tells a story or makes clear some point which your report is trying to explain. Consider the following statement which is taken from *An Essay on Animal Reproduction* written in 1768 by Spallanzani: *

> I have thought a sufficient number of figures [illustrations] would be of the greatest importance to the subject. If they are generally ornaments in [other] books of natural history, they may be said to be the life and spirit of mine.

Spallanzani is saying that in many science books the illustrations are just ornaments, but that in his book, they play an important part in what he is trying to show. Illustrations are "the life and spirit" of his writing.

2. Every illustration must show *clearly* what it is intended to show. The picture or drawing should be so clear and so pre-

---

* Lazaro Spallanzani (1729–1799), Italian naturalist and physiologist known for his work on life processes and normal functioning of animals, and for his proof that the theory of spontaneous generation was false (see also Redi, pp. 15–19 of this book, for information on the theory of spontaneous generation).

cise that explanations and descriptions can be reduced to a minimum, if not omitted entirely. Of course, a title is essential, but there should be as little additional explanation as possible. In order to be clear, the picture must be large enough to make every detail visible. Do not expect the reader to strain his eyes to see details. If some important part is too small in the illustration, it is wise to enlarge this part, and present it as an additional picture.

3. Every illustration should be *pleasing* to the eye. If you want the reader to look at your illustrations, you must make them attractive, pleasing, and maybe even artistic. This means that each figure should be simple, neat, well balanced, and well composed. Sloppy drawings will only detract from your report. Colored pictures are much more impressive and attractive than black and white, but don't overdo it. Color should not be used if it detracts from the usefulness or clarity of the picture.

Now that we understand what makes a good illustration, we can consider some of the kinds of illustrations which you may want to use in your report.

1. Photographs. You may find it possible to include in your report one or more photographs. For example, you might present a photograph showing an experimental animal placed side by side with a control animal to illustrate a difference between them. Or you might have photographs of the same animal before and after treatment. Photographs have many advantages. They are exact, and they enable you to present in your report a permanent record of some event which actually may have lasted for a very short time.

2. Drawings. Drawings are not quite as exact as photographs for showing what you saw; inaccuracies can creep in. On the other hand, they have certain advantages. While a photograph includes everything, you can emphasize in a drawing the important things and play down or omit the unimportant details; you can draw attention directly to the main idea which you want your picture to show. Naturally, your drawing must be as accurate as possible, and, of course, it must be neat and attractive.

3. Measureable records. In certain kinds of research, it is desirable to record on a moving tape the characteristic motion of the structure being studied. For example, in studies of heart action or muscle action it is common practice to use the motion of the organ to induce similar motion in a long lever which is in contact with a moving drum. The lever makes marks on the drum as the organ moves, and thus a visible record is made. Such a moving drum is called a kymograph, and the kymograph record may be made permanent. Similar records can be made in other ways and for other purposes. If your report deals with weather, you may want to include a barograph record of pressure; if it deals with earthquakes, you may want your report to show a tracing produced by a seismograph.

4. Graphs. A graph is actually a statistical picture. It is a graphic way of summarizing and presenting the information which you recorded in your tables. Since graphs make up a very important form of illustration in scientific reports, you should learn how to prepare and use several different types. The most important forms of graphs are illustrated in the next few pages.

a. *The bar graph* (Figure 19). A bar graph consists of a series of vertical (or horizontal) bars, each representing a number or a quantity. The height of a vertical bar (or length of a horizontal bar) represents a variable quantity shown on a scale. The bar begins at the zero line and ends at the number or quantity it represents. All the bars should be exactly the same in width. To make the bars stand out clearly from the rest of the graph, they are colored or shaded.

Sometimes bar graphs may also show an additional feature — the composition of a group. For example, in Figure 20, the various years are compared not only for total insurance purchases but also for relative proportions of ordinary, group, and industrial life insurance purchases. A bar graph of this type is often called a divided-bar graph.

These graphs can be made more dramatic and interesting by giving them a three-dimensional effect (Figure 21), or by using pictures to represent the units of the graph.

b. *The pictograph* (Figure 22). This type of graph is similar to a bar graph, but much more dramatic. Instead of a solid bar, it consists of a series of symbols. Each symbol is used to represent a given number or quantity, and it is repeated as many times as necessary to represent the total number in the category. Obviously, this type of graph has a great deal of eye appeal.

c. *The line graph* (Figure 23). This is the most commonly used type of graph. It is used to show how a quantity changes. It

FIGURE **19.** *A Bar Graph, Showing Alternate Usage of Vertical and Horizontal Bars*

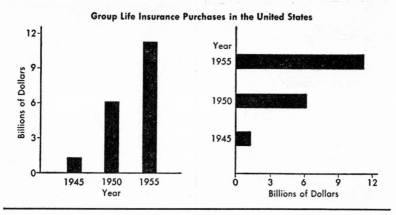

Group Life Insurance Purchases in the United States

FIGURE **20.** *A Divided-bar Graph*

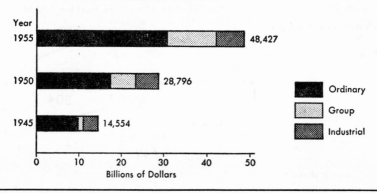

Life Insurance Purchases in the U. S.

FIGURE **21.**

A Three-dimensional Bar Graph. (Notice that the data used here is the same data given in Figure 19 and in part of Figure 20.)

Institute of Life Insurance

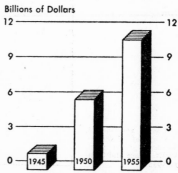

Group Life Insurance Purchases in the United States

Billions of Dollars

FIGURE **22.** *A Pictograph*

OUTPUT PER MAN·HOUR:
Key to future welfare

1850

1900

1930

1940

1950

1960

The Twentieth Century Fund

Each symbol represents 20 cents worth of output at 1947 prices.

FIGURE **23.** *A Line Graph*

Deaths Caused by Burning in Home Accidents, by Age, 1954

Hundreds of Deaths

14
12
10
8
6
4
2
0

| 0– 4 | 5– 14 | 15– 24 | 25– 44 | 45– 64 | 65 & over |

Years of Age

Accident Facts, National Safety Council, 1955

FIGURE **24.**
A Circle or Pie Graph

Where Federal Taxes Come From, Fiscal Year 1956–57

ESTIMATED

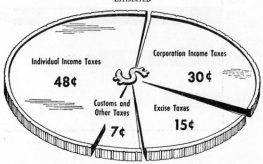

Individual Income Taxes
48¢

Corporation Income Taxes
30¢

Customs and Other Taxes
7¢

Excise Taxes
15¢

Bureau of the Budget

FIGURE **25.**
An Exploded-Map Graph

From Casner and Gabriel, *The Story of American Democracy*, 3rd edition, Harcourt, Brace and Company, 1955

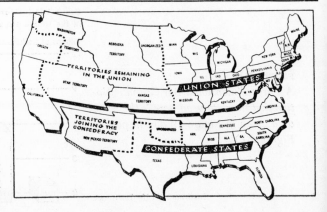

indicates a trend — an increase or decrease. It is excellent for comparing two or more groups which have been subjected to the same conditions.

There are various ways of dressing up line graphs. Lines of different color can be used. Or the lines may be drawn in different ways — solid, dotted, dash, dash-dot. A small diagram or caption can be put on the line to indicate what it represents. It can be presented in three-dimensional style to make it more outstanding.

d. *The circle graph or pie graph* (Figure 24). Such a graph is used to show the relationship between a part and the whole. The full circle (360°) represents the whole, and each sector represents a fraction or part of the whole. Thus, to represent 25 per cent of the whole, we use a sector of 90° out of the full circle. Here, too, color, shading, and stippling can be used to make the graph more striking and attractive. The three-dimensional effect can also be applied.

A similar type of graph may be made out of a map to show a distribution throughout the country. Many other variations are possible. Among the examples given is the " exploded " type of graph or map (Figure 25).

Whatever form of graph you may happen to use, there are some general rules to be followed. These rules or conventions were set up in order to provide a certain degree of uniformity so as to make the graphs more easily understandable to everyone.

    1. Arrange the material with the scales as follows (Figure 26):
      a. Vertical scale on left side, reading from the bottom up.
      b. Horizontal scale at the bottom of the graph, reading from left to right.

    2. Select the scale so that the zero point falls on the graph. If you cannot possibly get the whole graph on the paper, show a break — but show the zero point on the graph (Figure 27).

    3. Words and figures to identify the scales (Figure 28) should be so placed that they can be read horizontally (for horizontal scales), and from the bottom of the page upward by turning the page clockwise (for vertical scales).

    4. Important lines such as the vertical and horizontal axes and the curve of the graph should be drawn darker and heavier than other lines in the graph (as, for instance, the lines on graph paper), so that they stand out clearly (Figure 29).

FIGURE **26.** *How to Place the Scales on a Graph*

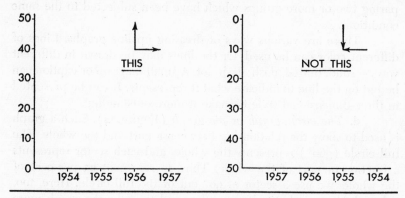

FIGURE **27.** *How to Place a Broken Scale on a Graph*

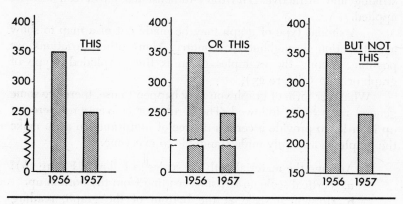

FIGURE **28.** *How to Label Scales on a Graph*

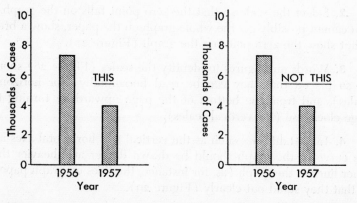

124

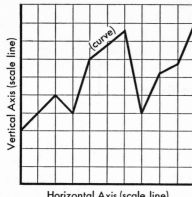

FIGURE **29.**
How to Emphasize the Scale Lines and Curve on a Graph When Using Ruled Paper

5. To plot a point on a graph, locate it first by reading to the right on the horizontal scale, then up on the vertical scale. To remember this procedure, think of this phrase: " Read right up." For example, in Figure 30, a sales total of $80,000 for June, 1957, is located by reading to the right to reach the month of June and then up to reach the $80,000 mark.

6. The formula of the curve, or a title, or an explanation may be written on the curve, especially if there is more than one curve on the same graph.

7. The whole graph should have a clear, concise title, which is as complete as possible (Figures 19 through 25).

FIGURE **30.** *How to Plot a Point on a Graph*

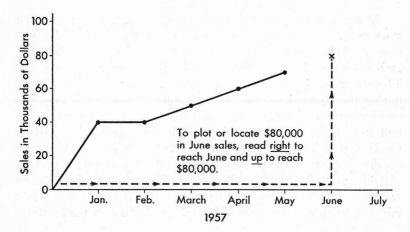

23 Analyzing the Data

        At some time during your work, you will find it necessary to analyze the raw data which you have collected. By *raw* data we mean the figures recorded in your " log " or in your tables. Up to this time, the data have been untouched, but you must now analyze them to see if they lead to a conclusion.

        Actually, analyzing raw data is nothing new to you. You have done it many times before in your life, although you may not have thought of it in this way. Consider the following situation as an example. Let us suppose that six weeks after the school term begins in September, one of your teachers asks you to tell him what mark you think you deserve for your work up to this point. How do you go about reaching your estimate?

        To begin with, you collect all the raw data that might have bearing on your mark. Thus, your teacher gave fifteen short tests during this period, and your marks were 9, 8, 10, 7, 6, 10, 10, 10, 9, 7, 10, 9, 9, 8, 10. He gave one long unit test on which you got a mark of 87 per cent. In addition, you did your homework regularly, you participated actively in class discussions, and you made a special report to the class for which you got a mark of 95 per cent.

        Without going into the whole problem of determining what mark you are worth, let us consider one bit of analysis which you must do. What do the fifteen quiz marks tell about you? Actually, each mark individually tells very little. But taken as a group, the fifteen marks tell how consistently you have been doing your work during the six-week period. So, although a single mark does not mean very much, the *average* of all fifteen marks is a very important item to be considered. To find the average of these fifteen marks, you add them all together, and divide by fifteen. When you do this, you are actually analyzing raw data. You get an average of 8.8 for your short tests, or 88 per cent. Your mark on the unit test was 87 per cent, and on your special report a bit higher. You might tell your teacher that you should get a " B " for the six weeks' work.

So you see, there is nothing mysterious about analyzing data. It is something which everyone does many times in his life. But for scientific work, we must understand clearly what we are doing, and why we are doing it. Our analysis must be accurate and clear cut, and in order to make it so we use a branch of mathematics called *statistics*. Statistics is sometimes defined as *the science of drawing inferences from observations*. One can spend many years studying the subject of statistics, but now it will be sufficient to understand the four statistical ideas which follow.

1. Statistics can tell you how your data groups around a common center. For example, suppose you measure one thousand leaves from a certain oak tree. You may want to know the average size, or what size occurs most frequently, or some other similar fact. To find out, you will make use of a *measure of central tendency*.

2. Statistics can also tell you how your data spread away from the common center. In the case of the one thousand leaves, you may want to know not only what size leaf occurs most frequently, but also what are the largest and smallest leaves. Or you may want to know how close to the average the other members of the group are. For this purpose, you will determine the spread of the group by using some *measure of variability*.

3. Statistics can be used to find out if there is a tendency for two things to go together, or to be related. For example, you might want to know if the difference in size of the leaves is in any way related to the height above the ground of the branch which bore them, or if the size of a leaf is related to its distance away from the trunk of the tree. To determine such relationships, you may make use of some *measure of correlation*.

4. Statistics can help you determine whether your results are accurate and reliable. Suppose you repeat the same experiment again, what is the likelihood that it will come out the same way? In the case of the leaves, suppose you took another one thousand leaves from another tree. How similar would the second group be to the first? For this purpose you will want to make use of some *measure of reliability*.

This is only a basic outline. If your work requires analysis, you must know more about these four statistical measures. Therefore, a special appendix on "The Fundamentals of Statistics" has been provided at the end of this book.

24 Sources of Error

Someone once said that as long as man is in search of knowledge he will make mistakes. This is as true of science research as it is of any other search for knowledge. According to Nobel Prize winner Charles Nicolle,* "Error is all around us, and creeps in at the least opportunity." Don't worry too much about the danger of making mistakes. It is better to carry on your work and make errors than to be so cautious and so careful that you don't do anything at all. However, there are certain kinds of errors which you can avoid by careful planning.

To begin with, there are errors which are due to carelessness. These are and can be prevented by simple precautions taken in advance. For example, the mere presence on your work table of extra chemicals and supplies may lead to errors. It is very easy to pick up the wrong bottle, and of course the wrong bottle has the wrong chemical. Such an error can easily be avoided if you make sure that your table is clear of everything except what you will need.

While we are on the subject of chemicals, you should learn not to put down on the table the stopper of the bottle from which you are pouring. For one thing, the stopper may pick up from the table all sorts of particles which will contaminate the chemical in the bottle. Even worse, if you put down two corks, you may eventually put the wrong corks in the wrong bottles and spoil both chemicals.

Another careless error is mixing up the experimental and control parts of an experiment. For example, suppose your labels are on covers which you have on the two parts of your experiment. You uncover both parts to add something, and then put the covers on in reverse. The next time you look, you are in trouble — trouble due to carelessness. To avoid this type of error, you should place your

* Charles Jean Henri Nicolle (1866–1936). French physician and bacteriologist; discovered that typhus fever is transmitted by the body louse. He was awarded the 1928 Nobel Prize for physiology and medicine.

labels so that they stay with the proper containers or parts of your experiment at all times. Color is very useful for avoiding error. For example, if your experiment involves two dishes of protozoa, or two Petri dishes of bacteria, you might use a red pencil to label the control part, and a blue pencil to label the experimental part. If you are using animals such as rats, mark them with harmless stains.

Arithmetic causes many careless errors. Addition, subtraction, multiplication, and division are simple processes, it is true. Yet people, including scientists, often make careless errors. The only way to avoid them is to check every calculation by another method.

Seemingly unimportant details, like visitors who smoke in the laboratory while you are working, may spoil your results. Someone may poke a tobacco-stained finger into a dish or accidentally flip a bit of cigar ash into your culture (Figure 31). These tiny bits of foreign substance may alter everything, and because you are unaware of their presence, they may lead you into error.

Another cause of contamination is poorly washed dishes. A dish may look perfectly clean, and yet it may retain tiny traces of whatever was in it before. It is surprising how certain chemicals cling to glass. One laboratory advises its technicians to use a special cleaning fluid, and to follow this with seventy rinses of hot and cold water, plus thirty rinses with distilled water. Did you ever wash a dish and then rinse it a hundred times? This particular laboratory does not believe a dish can really be clean unless you do just that!

However, errors may stem from other sources besides carelessness. Many of these sources are a little more subtle, and therefore a little harder to detect. For example, in selecting subjects for an experiment, how do you know that the subjects are normal and typical of the general population? Obviously, if your subjects are not typical, then your results will certainly not be typical. For example, if a scientist is testing the value of penicillin, and he happens to use as his subject a person who is allergic to penicillin, he is apt to conclude that penicillin is a dangerous drug. In selecting the subjects for an experiment, presumably we select *normal* individuals. But remember that there is a great deal of variation among normal members of a group. Whenever possible, use large groups of subjects, rather than single individuals.

Here is still another source of error which can be made in the best of laboratories. Suppose the effect of a certain drug is being tested on some animal or plant. A small dose may cause a certain reaction, while a large dose may produce a completely different

FIGURE **31**. *Carelessness is costly. In what way may the friend of the youthful experimenter shown here be spoiling the results of an experiment?*

effect. Or the same chemical may affect one part of a plant in one way, and another part of the same plant in a different way. For example, certain plant hormones will make the stem of a plant turn upward, while at the same time making the root turn downward.

Other errors are caused by the fact that the experimenter doesn't know certain information which he should know. Here is a classic example of such an error made in 1767 by the famous physician and scientist, Dr. John Hunter. In order to study the disease known as gonorrhea, Dr. Hunter intentionally infected himself with the pus from one of his diseased patients. What he did not know was that the patient was also suffering from syphilis, a completely different disease. Soon, the symptoms of both diseases began to show themselves, but since Dr. Hunter thought he had infected himself with a single disease, he concluded that all these symptoms belonged to one disease. This error, caused by insufficient knowledge, persisted in medicine for many years after Dr. Hunter reported his findings.

Obviously, this chapter cannot deal with all the possible sources of error. However, if you are aware of some of them, you will be better able to avoid them. Don't let fear of error frighten you away from doing things because, in the words of a famous mathematician, " Panic of error is the death of progress."

25 Formulating the Conclusion

Once you have organized the facts which you have discovered and have analyzed your results carefully, you are ready to come to a conclusion. You should now be able to arrive at some kind of answer to your original question.

Actually, if you have planned your investigation properly, you have already anticipated certain possible results, and you have already thought about the several different conclusions which you *might* reach (see Chapter 17). Now, however, is the time to decide which of these conclusions is actually indicated by the results. It is possible that the results do not point to any of the conclusions which you anticipated. In such a case, you must be ready to throw away all the conclusions which you had thought about, and reach a new conclusion which is based on these unexpected results.

Since you are probably a beginner in the art of drawing conclusions from observed facts, you may be influenced by your personality and by your outlook on things in general. If you are the perennial optimist, the "bubbling-over" type, you may be inclined to jump at conclusions. You may fall prey to what Dr. Bernhard Steinberg * calls "The Run-Away Attitude" (Figure 32). On the other hand, if you are the wary type, the too cautious worrier, you may be inclined to bend over backwards to avoid reaching a conclusion. This, Dr. Steinberg calls "The Lean-Backwards Attitude" (Figure 33).

You can readily see that the attitudes illustrated in Figures 32 and 33 are rather extreme. It is very tempting to jump to a conclusion based on meager data and isolated facts, especially if they point toward the result you think you ought to get. Jumping at a conclusion is an easy way out. It relieves your mind of all worry, of all

---

* Dr. Bernhard Steinberg is Director of the Toledo Hospital Institute of Medical Research, Toledo, Ohio.

THE RUN-AWAY ATTITUDE OR
FLIGHT OF THE IMAGINATION

Ah, a discovery! A plant and a dead chicken close by. Must be a deadly species of drug in the plant. One smell and poof! A chicken that smells and a plant that kills in a single smell. Wonderful! A great discovery. Enough material for a book.

Redrawn by permission of Bernhard Steinberg, M.D., from his book, *It was My Idea.*

FIGURE 32. *No scientist would approach a problem in this way! Would you?*

the discomfort of doubt — but don't do it. Don't be like the man who said, "All Indians walk in single file." When asked what evidence he had for this, he replied, "The one I saw did." On the other hand, it is just as bad to be a "doubting Thomas." Don't bend over backwards so far that you fall flat on your back. You will never reach a conclusion this way. There is absolutely nothing wrong with stating that your conclusion is a tentative one, subject to further checking and investigation. Nor is there any objection to explaining that your conclusion is limited by many factors which you realize may make the conclusion inaccurate. Try to reach a conclusion which is a direct outgrowth of only the observed facts.

Redrawn by permission of Bernhard Steinberg, M.D., from his book, *It was My Idea*.

FIGURE **33.** *Can you explain why a scientist would never have this kind of attitude toward a problem?*

Another danger that you must learn to avoid is that of making your conclusion too broad. For example, if you treat bean seedlings with a chemical called *AMMO–1618* and you find that the plants are dwarfed, you have no right to conclude that *AMMO–1618* dwarfs plants. You can only draw a conclusion about bean plants. After all, you did not try it on coleus, or bluegrass, or gladioli, or any of the millions of other varieties of plants, and you do not know what effect it will have on them. *A conclusion is valid only for the precise conditions of the experiment.*

Here is a rather ridiculous case which illustrates that a conclusion is valid only for the precise conditions of the experiment. Suppose a cage is prepared with two feeding stations, but station A is so wired that an animal going there gets a severe electric shock. Now some nice red meat is put into feeding station A, and Blanko dog biscuits are put into station B. Then a hungry dog is allowed to wander freely in the cage and "choose the food he likes." It is observed that every one of the five hundred dogs tested ends up by choosing Blanko dog biscuits instead of meat. Would it be reasonable to conclude that *dogs prefer Blanko dog biscuits to meat?* A moment's thought will show you that this is not a fair conclusion to draw. But it would be perfectly valid to conclude that *dogs prefer Blanko dog biscuits to meat when they get an electric shock as a result of choosing meat*. The conclusion must reflect the exact conditions of the experiment.

There are many situations in which the outlook for a good conclusion looks hopeless. Things didn't work out the way you had hoped. Or maybe they didn't work out at all. But don't get discouraged — you are in good company. Not all investigations turn out successfully, even in the hands of expert scientists. So why should you expect success the first time? Of course, most of us hear only about the *successful* experiments, and this gives us the false idea that research is easy. It isn't. Yet things may not be as black as they seem. Perhaps you have a conclusion after all. Even the statement, "This experiment failed to answer the question for which it was intended," is a conclusion. Perhaps this "failure" will suggest a new and better approach to the problem. Consider the following words of Joseph Priestley,* stated in 1772:

> Very lame and imperfect theories are sufficient to suggest useful experiments which serve to correct those theories, and give birth to others more perfect. These then occasion further experiments, which bring us still nearer to the truth; and in this method of approximation, we must be content to proceed. And we ought to think ourselves happy, if, in this slow method, we make any real progress.

It is possible that a negative conclusion may be just as important as a positive conclusion. Take the following case, for example. A boy knows that the drug *dramamine* is used to prevent

---

* Joseph Priestley (1733–1804), English clergyman and chemist. He announced the discovery of "dephlogisticated air" in 1774 but did not know he had actually isolated one of a mixture of elements which make up the atmosphere. In France, Antoine Laurent Lavoisier (1743–1794) performed experiments resulting in the isolation of what he recognized as a separate element, now called oxygen. Actually Lavoisier's oxygen and Priestley's "dephlogisticated air" were one and the same.

seasickness or car sickness. He reasons that dramamine slows down the reactions of the body. Now, he wonders whether he can make use of this information. Perhaps dramamine can also be used to slow down the reactions of a paramecium, and thus make it easier to study under the microscope. So, he sets up an experiment in which he adds varying amounts of dramamine to different paramecium cultures. Lo and behold, the little animals continue to swim about as fast as ever.

Should the boy classify his experiment as a failure? On the contrary, he can reach a good and valid conclusion. *He can state that within the limits of the experiment dramamine has no observable effect on paramecia.* His result was negative, it is true, but negative results have their value, too. It is just as important to know what a certain drug does *not* do as it is to know what it does. Furthermore, a negative result may lead to additional fruitful experimentation. In this case, the boy may be led to wonder why dramamine affects humans but apparently not paramecia. As a result, he may plan an experiment to find out *how* dramamine causes its effect (which may be more important in the long run than what effect it has).

Of course, the fact that you are unable to demonstrate by your experiment that a certain hypothesis is correct does not necessarily prove that the hypothesis is wrong. Somebody else, using better techniques, or the right materials, or a more suitable experiment may be able to prove the theory to be correct. By the same token, the fact that your experiment does support a hypothesis does not necessarily prove that the hypothesis is correct. You must learn to approach your results with a healthy degree of skepticism. According to Michael Faraday, " He is the wisest philosopher who holds his theory with some doubt."

Be skeptical of your results, but not as skeptical as the boy described below. He had read that alcohol is harmful, and he set out to see if he could show this experimentally. He set up two cages, each containing three pregnant female rats. Into one cage he caused alcohol fumes to be blown constantly, so that the rats in this cage were forced to take in alcohol as they breathed. The control cage did not have alcohol in the air. When the rats gave birth, he found that those mothers which had been exposed to alcohol gave birth to smaller litters — but the young rats of alcoholic mothers grew bigger and lived longer (on the average) than the controls! The boy wrote his conclusion as shown at the top of the next page.

My experiment did not come out the way it should. From my reading I know that alcohol is harmful, so it is impossible for the children of the alcoholic mothers to be healthier than the children of the controls. My experiment should show that rats are harmed by exposure to alcohol.

Obviously this "experimenter" was very unscientific. He refused to believe his eyes; he preferred to accept what he had read in a book. Authorities had stated that the rats should be harmed by alcohol, so he preferred to think that his experiment was wrong. Perhaps his experiment *was* wrong. Still, he had no right to conclude how it *should* have come out. He should have drawn conclusions only from what actually occurred. His conclusion might better have read as follows:

This experiment seems to indicate that in rats the offspring of alcoholic mothers grow larger and live longer than the offspring of non-alcoholic mothers. However, these results do not seem to agree with what I have read. Most authorities say that alcohol is harmful. I think my experiment should be repeated several times, to see if it will come out the same way again, or if this result was just an accident.

Just as it is wrong for the experimenter to refuse to believe the results of his experiment, so it is bad for him to take too much credit. It is very easy to accept the credit for something which nature is accomplishing without your help (or perhaps even in spite of your interference). Consider the case where a certain drug is fed to anemic rabbits, and a rise in red blood corpuscles is observed. Are you justified in concluding that the drug caused the improvement? Or is it just as possible that the normal body processes of the rabbits were taking care of the matter and that the increase in red corpuscles would have occurred as well without the drug as with it?

Another common mistake in drawing conclusions is to assume that because two things occur together, one must be the cause of the other. Suppose A and B occur at the same time. Does this prove that A caused B; or that B caused A; or that they caused each other? It might prove any one of these things, but then again A and B may have no relationship to each other. They may occur together by coincidence. Suppose you make a survey of your geometry class, and you find that those students who smoke make lower grades in geometry than nonsmokers. Does it follow that smoking causes poor work in geometry? Do you think so? Well, consider this case. There has been a great increase in the use of dental X rays in the United States, and this increase parallels the rise in heart disease. Are we justified in concluding that dental X rays cause heart disease? Hardly! So, be very careful that you do not fall into a trap when you draw a conclusion in your own experiment. Remember that when two things occur together, one *may be* the cause of the other, but on the other hand, the two things may have no relationship whatsoever.

When you find that a relationship *does* exist, be sure to state it correctly. Consider the following case. A man pointed his finger at a frog and shouted, " Jump! " The frog jumped. Then the man cut off the frog's hind legs. Again he pointed his finger at the frog and shouted, " Jump! " But this time the frog did not jump. " See! " exclaimed the man in triumph. " I have just proved that when you cut off the legs of a frog he becomes quite deaf! "

One last thing. You must be very careful to distinguish between assumption and fact when you are drawing conclusions. Michael Faraday once put it this way: ". . . be most careful . . . to distinguish the knowledge which consists of assumption . . . from that which is the knowledge of facts and laws." It is easy to start with some basic assumption at the beginning of an experiment. The trick is to remember at the end that we began with an assumption. Obviously, the conclusion we reach can only be valid if the original assumption is correct. Therefore, in stating the conclusion, you must make clear whether or not there are any basic assumptions upon which the whole procedure and conclusion are based.

26 Reporting the Results — Introductory Statement

The final step in any piece of scientific research is reporting the results. There is nothing to be gained by hiding or concealing the outcome of your research. In fact, secrecy is against the spirit of science. Every speck of new knowledge illuminates the dark corners around it where knowledge is lacking. Every new discovery, no matter how small, may open new fields for study.

Generally speaking, there are two ways in which scientists make their work known to the world:

1. The written report. A scientist may write a report, describing his experiment, for publication in one of the many scientific magazines. Sometimes a brief preliminary report or progress report is printed even before the work is actually finished. Such a preliminary report can be criticized by others, and the criticisms may reveal weaknesses which can still be corrected before it is too late. Usually, however, the printed report is a final account of work completed. As a high school " scientist," you may be called upon to write a report of your research for publication in your school magazine; or you may be required to submit a report of your investigation to the judges of a science scholarship competition; or your teacher may want you to leave a written record of your work for use by younger pupils in subsequent terms.

2. An oral report at a science congress. In this case, the scientist appears as a speaker before a group of other scientists. He delivers his report orally, using whatever materials may make it more interesting or more understandable. Following the report, there are questions and criticisms from the audience. The scientist has a chance to answer the questions and reply to the criticisms. In your case, you may be asked to deliver a report on your research to your class, to your science club, or before a student assembly.

You may also want to present your work at a science fair, or to a science congress attended by science-minded pupils of many different schools.

Regardless of which method you will be called on to use, there is one important thing which you must keep in mind. Remember that you are an "expert" on the subject. After all, you have discussed the problem, analyzed it, and thought about it. You have read everything about it that you could get your hands on. You have lived with it, slept with it, and worried about it. Your fellow students have not; they know very little about the subject. They are unfamiliar with the terms which you have learned to use freely.

What would be your reaction if a fellow student reporting orally to the class made the following remark: "Aminopterin is a folic acid antagonist, intraperitoneal injection of which results in a competitive blocking of the normal metabolism of the leucocytes."? You would probably say that the boy is trying to show off how many big words he knows. Yet, to a person who has read a great deal about the action of the drug aminopterin, the sentence has a very definite meaning. However, most students have not read a great deal about aminopterin. In fact, it is likely that most students never even heard of it. So you cannot expect them to understand such a statement on your part.

In a way it is unfortunate that scientists have developed a vocabulary and a language of their own. This language is so strange to the average person that he is frightened by it. He is so overwhelmed by the words that he cannot get to the *simple basic idea* which is usually hidden underneath. Of course, a research scientist writing for other research scientists in the same field can assume that his readers will understand the "foreign language" which he writes. But you are writing for the average person. You cannot assume that the average person will have the special knowledge to understand the special vocabulary. So make it a rule to say what you have to say in as simple a way as possible. A good question to keep in mind at all times is this: Would this report be clear to me if I knew only as much about the subject as the person who will read it, or the person who will hear me speak? Keeping this question in mind at all times, let us now consider what should be included in the report which you prepare to cover your investigation. Chapters 27 and 28 will deal with the written report, and Chapter 29 with the oral report.

27 The Written Report

When you get ready to write a report of your investigation, you are sure to ask yourself, "What form should I use?" The answer is quite simple: there is no single correct form for a scientific report. Leeuwenhoek described his discoveries in long, drawn-out letters addressed to the Secretary of the Royal Society of London. William Harvey described his famous experiments on the circulation of blood in a treatise addressed "To the Most Illustrious and Indomitable Prince Charles, King of Great Britain, France, and Ireland, Defender of Faith." Many scientists presented their findings in books which they themselves published. In modern times scientific papers are published in magazines. Regardless of their form, they all have one thing in common. This was very well stated by Spallanzani in his *Essay on Animal Reproduction*. He said:

> As several of the results of my experiments appear singular, I shall make it my business to describe them with precision, to mention the precautions and means I have used in making these observations, the temperature of the air, and the situation proper for the animals together with the food I gave them; and in short, to disclose all the circumstances which may contribute to the understanding and establishing of the facts, so that the lovers of natural history on repeating my experiments, may, if they please, confirm and extend them still further. . . .

As you see, the major purpose of a report is to present your findings in such clear detail that any other person with the desire and the ability can repeat your experiment and check your results. In order to achieve this purpose, your report must include certain minimum essentials, which are outlined below.

1. Title. Your report should have an appropriate title which indicates clearly what it concerns.

2. Introduction. You should begin with some sort of introductory statement in which you deal with such questions as how you came to select this particular problem, and why you think it is worth spending time on. Usually the writer gives a little historical background, in which he describes previous work in the field, and/or basic information. It is important to give proper credit to others for previous work, for assistance, and for ideas. Taking credit for yourself for ideas or work done by others is dishonest, and goes against the grain for all true scientists.

3. The problem. The introduction leads to a clear statement of the specific problem (see Chapter 13) which you have attacked.

4. The materials and the methods. The statement of the problem is followed by a detailed description of the materials used and the methods employed. This description must be so exact and so complete that anyone who wants to do so can repeat your experiment. Just remember Spallanzani's words: ". . . I shall make it my business . . . to disclose all the circumstances . . . so that the lovers of natural history, on repeating my experiments, may . . . confirm and extend them . . ." Often a photograph or a diagram of your setup can save a great many words of description.

5. The observations. Naturally, you must report what happened. How you summarize your results will depend on the type of investigation you have carried out, but pictures and tables (see Chapters 21 and 22) are always appropriate. Here is where you must be especially careful that you are saying precisely what you mean to say. Most words have more than one dictionary meaning, and perhaps even more meanings in popular usage. To say something so that it cannot be misunderstood requires that you be absolutely clear yourself on what you mean to say, and that you say it in clear, simple, unmistakable terms.

6. Analysis of the results. After you have summarized your observations, you are ready to analyze and interpret them. It may be helpful to use graphs (see Chapter 22) to help make clear the direction in which your results point.

7. The conclusion. The analysis of the results leads to a statement of the conclusion (see Chapters 23, 24, and 25). You should give the line of reasoning — the logic — which leads you to reach the conclusion.

8. Limitations. The logic by which you reached your conclusion may have some flaws; or you may realize that your experiment had certain weaknesses. This is the time to state the limitations of your conclusion and the sources of error which weaken your results. It is better to state these limitations yourself than to have somebody else point them out later. As Michael Faraday once said, one should "criticize one's own view in every way . . . if possible leave no objection to be put by others."

9. Implications and applications. In the light of the weaknesses and limitations of your experiment, what are the implications? Can you suggest any further research along these lines? Are there any practical applications which may grow out of this work? Do not hesitate to state them.

10. Summary. Often, a scientific paper ends with a brief summary of the high lights which were described in the full report.

11. Bibliography. Last but not least, it is desirable and necessary to list all the references which you used in your work. These references are usually listed in alphabetical order (by author's name) at the end of the report. If the reference is a book, you should state author, title, publisher, date, place of publication, and pages cited. In the case of magazine articles, you should state author, title of article, name of magazine, date and number of the issue, and page numbers. Here is a sample bibliography as it might appear at the end of a written report dealing with heredity:

1. Beadle, George W., "Biochemical Genetics," Chemical Reviews, Vol. 37, No. 1, Aug. 1945, pp. 15–96

2. Brooklyn Botanic Garden, "The Birth of Genetics," Genetics, Vol. 35, No. 5, part 2, Sept. 1950

3. Goldstein, Philip, Genetics Is Easy, Lantern Press (New York), 1955

4. Harbou, D. J., "Gregor Johann Mendel," The Scientific Monthly, Vol. 40, No. 4, April 1935, pp. 313–322

5. Scheinfeld, Amram, The New You and Heredity, J. B. Lippincott Co. (Philadelphia, Pa.), 1950, and The Human Heredity Handbook, J. B. Lippincott Co., 1956

6. Cook, Robert, "A Chronology of Genetics," from Better Plants and Animals: Yearbook of Agriculture, U.S. Department of Agriculture, Vol. 2, 1937, pp. 1457–1477

You will note that in this bibliography, Nos. 1, 2, and 4 are articles from magazines, Nos. 3 and 5 are books, and No. 6 is a chapter in a book. While the numbers which appear before the names of the authors in this list are not essential, they are useful when you want to indicate the authority for a certain statement in the body of your report. Thus, for example, suppose the following statement appears in your report: " Even protozoa give definite evidence that sex is inherited. (1)(3)." This means that Beadle's article (No. 1 in the bibliography) and Goldstein's book (No. 3 in the bibliography) are the sources from which you got the information for this particular statement. It is customary, in writing scientific reports, to give credit in this fashion.

If you have studied this chapter and digested its contents, you are probably ready to write a report of your project. After it is written, perhaps you ought to re-examine the finished product before you hand it in to your teacher or send it to the judges. Here is a check list which will help you evaluate your finished report.

1. Is the report attractive in appearance?

    a. Is it neat?
    b. Is it legible?
    c. If typed, is the report double spaced and on one side of the paper only?
    d. Are the margins at sides, top, and bottom, wide enough?

2. Is the report well written?

    a. Is it written in good English?
    b. Is the spelling correct?
    c. Is the punctuation correct?
    d. Is it interesting? (There is no reason why a scientific report cannot be interesting as well as accurate.)
    e. Is it written in your own words? (The worst possible thing you can do in your report is to copy someone else's words and claim they are your own.)
    f. Is it written in language which your fellow classmates can understand?
    g. Does it stick to the topic?
    h. Is the material presented logically?
    i. Does the report say what you want it to say?

3. Is the form of the report suitable for its purpose?

    a. Does it begin with an appropriate title?

    b. Is the problem clearly stated?

    c. Does the conclusion answer the question in the problem?

    d. Is the conclusion supported by the evidence in the form of data derived from the experiment?

    e. Are the data accurately stated?

    f. Are the data presented in a form which the reader will readily grasp and understand?

    g. Has proper credit been given to others for facts, statements, ideas, and advice?

    h. Is the bibliography properly stated?

4. Would this report be clear to me if I knew about the subject only as much as the reader knows?

Having considered some of the requirements of a good written report, let us now look at an example of a written report prepared by a student. The next chapter is devoted to this sample report.

28 A Sample Written Report

It might help you in writing your own report if you read and analyze two or three reports written by other students of your age. One such report is included here for your convenience. Read this report and analyze it. See if it fulfills all the requirements of a good report as set down in Chapter 27. Perhaps you will be able to find certain faults. If you do, ask yourself how you would overcome these flaws. But at all times, keep this question in mind as you read — " Did the person who wrote the report make clear to me what he wanted to say? "

THE EFFECT OF CHLOROPHYLL CONTENT OF LEAVES
ON INFRARED PHOTOGRAPHS
by S————— B————

Introduction
    During a class discussion in chemistry, my teacher mentioned the fact that infrared photography could be used to detect camouflage. He said that this was possible be-cause the chlorophyll in the foliage reflects infrared light and photographs white, while camouflage paint absorbs infrared and photographs black.
    This statement interested me. I have always been a "camera-bug," and I frequently wondered about infrared photography. Here was a chance to explore the field and to apply my hobby to a scientific problem. I thought about it a great deal, and set to work gathering as much information as I possibly could.

Background Information
    It is a well-known fact that white light is really a mixture of lights of many colors. This can be demonstrated by passing white light through a triangular prism. It is

broken up into a band of colored light as shown in the diagram below. This band of colored light is called the visible spectrum.

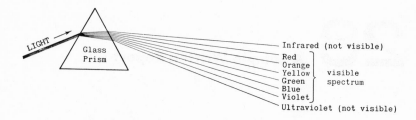

The prism is able to separate white light into its separate colored parts, because each color represents light of a different wave length. These wave lengths range from 400 millimicrons at the violet end to 700 millimicrons at the red end. Since the prism causes the light of each wave length to bend a different amount, each color is separated out from the mixture which exists in white light. These colors represent only the _visible_ light rays. There are other rays which are _not_ visible. Below the visible violet there are rays with wave lengths still shorter than 400 millimicrons, such as ultraviolet rays. At the other end, there is a region of invisible radiation known as the infrared region, with wave lengths longer than 700 millimicrons. This region extends indefinitely, and as the wave length increases, the radiation emerges as heat waves, and then radio waves. However, only the infrared region between 700 and 900 millimicrons is of use photographically. My project concerns itself with photographs taken in this region.

Infrared radiation may behave quite differently from visible radiation. This fact is shown most vividly in infrared photographs of foliage. This is due to the behavior of the green coloring of the leaves. This green coloring, called chlorophyll, absorbs a large percentage of the visible light which falls upon it. Therefore, foliage appears dark in a panchromatic photograph. But chlorophyll does not absorb the invisible infrared radiation. On the contrary, most of the infrared is reflected by the chlorophyll, and, therefore, on infrared sensitive plates, foliage appears light in color.

The Problem

Now that I was aware of this special effect of chlorophyll on infrared radiation, it occurred to me that I might be able to use infrared photography to determine the _amount_ of chlorophyll in a leaf. I reasoned that a leaf with more chlorophyll should reflect more infrared than a leaf with less chlorophyll, and I wondered whether this difference would show up in an infrared photograph. I set myself the problem of finding out whether different species of leaves would photograph with different degrees of brightness because of differences in chlorophyll content.

This idea received support from a series of infrared aerial photographs which were taken of the Harvard Forest. In these photographs, areas of hardwood trees appeared nearly white, while areas of softwood trees appeared gray to black. Thus, in these aerial photos it was possible to distinguish different kinds of trees by studying the infrared photographs. In fact, various species of softwoods could be distinguished on the basis of tone of gray. In another study, long-range infrared photographs were taken from ground level. It was found that, in general, deciduous vegetation reflects well and photographs light, while evergreens are poor reflectors and photograph dark. I thought I could test these two observations as well.

Method and Observations

In order to carry out my experiment, I collected seven kinds of leaves common to my neighborhood. I made sure that some were softwoods and others hardwoods; that some were from deciduous trees while others were from evergreen. Then I photographed each leaf with film sensitive to infrared radiation. I used Kodak I.R. 135 film, with a Kodak A filter. The filter is necessary because infrared film is also sensitive in the blue region. Since for this project I wanted the pictures taken entirely by infrared radiation, I used the filter to absorb the blue light.

The first seven photographs (Nos. 1-7) were taken with light from two No. 2 floods in reflectors, set up as in the diagram below. The lights were 3 feet from the leaves, and at a 45° angle to them. The camera was placed $3\frac{1}{2}$ feet from the leaves, and the exposure was $\frac{1}{6}$ of a second at f/4. Photographs were taken of the following leaves:

Photo Number	Species	Wood type	Leaves
1	Poplar	Soft	Deciduous
2	Red Maple	Hard	Deciduous
3	Sycamore	Hard	Deciduous
4	Blue Spruce	Soft	Evergreen
5	Rhododendron	Shrub	Evergreen
6	Magnolia	Soft	Evergreen
7	Black Oak	Hard	Deciduous

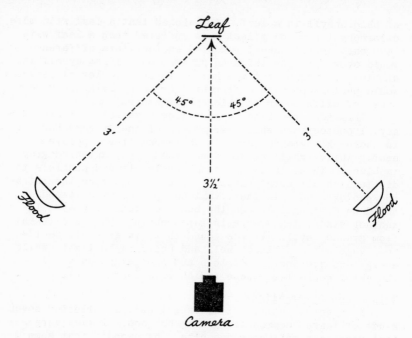

Upon observing the photographs (Nos. 1–7), I could find no obvious difference in brightness. This is quite evident from photographs Nos. 1–7 which are attached. [Note — at this point in the original report, infrared photographs of seven leaves were attached.]

I now moved the camera closer to the leaves, and photographed the leaves again. This time with the camera only 10 inches from the leaves, I used an exposure of ½ second at f/7. This second set of photographs (Nos. 1A–7A) is also attached. In this series the maple (No. 2A), the spruce (No. 4A), and the rhododendron (No. 5A) appear equally bright, while the sycamore (No. 3A) and the oak (No. 7A) appear considerably darker.

There are two possible explanations for the fact that no difference in brightness was visible when the photographs were taken at 3½ feet, while a visible difference does appear at 10 inches:

1. It is possible that the exposures while enlarging were not perfectly controlled.

2. It is possible that the difference in brightness is actually due to differences in the amount of chlorophyll.

To check whether a true difference exists, I placed a sycamore leaf and maple leaf side by side and photographed them. The exposure was ½ second at f/7. Photograph No.

2.3B shows that the maple leaf appeared very slightly brighter than the sycamore. I now placed the oak leaf side by side with the spruce, and photographed them as above. Photograph No. 4.7B shows that the spruce appears slightly brighter than the oak. But in neither case is the difference very outstanding.

Conclusion

From these experiments, I concluded that all the leaves I photographed appeared almost equally bright, with very little variation from species to species. Only the sycamore and oak seemed a shade darker than the others. Therefore, this method does not appear to be satisfactory for distinguishing different species of leaves, or hard-woods from softwoods, or evergreens from deciduous trees. In this respect, my results differ from those reported for aerial photographs. Perhaps aerial photographs make a distinction where large masses of leaves are involved, but my photographs of single leaves did not.

Furthermore, my photographs did not seem to show much variation in the chlorophyll content of the different leaves. Curiosity about this led me to do additional library research to find out whether any work had been done to compare the chlorophyll content of different leaves. I had little success. I consulted several books on plant physiology, and I searched through many issues of Biological Abstracts, but I could not find any information. Upon inquiring at the Brooklyn Botanic Garden, I was referred to Dr. ————, who explained to me that such studies were difficult because the chlorophyll content of a leaf varies with environmental conditions. For example, a sycamore growing in shade produces a different amount of chlorophyll from a sycamore growing in direct sunlight. Water, soil, and a leaf's position on the tree are other factors involved.

After my conversation with Dr. ————, I began to realize that I should have determined the chlorophyll content of each leaf before I photographed it. If I could find a way of determining chlorophyll content of a series of leaves, I could then see if there is a corresponding difference in brightness as shown on infrared photographs. It would also help if I had a densitometer with which to measure more accurately the brightness of the photographs. I am now in the process of beginning over again with this new idea in mind.

Summary

1. Leaves of seven species of trees were photographed with infrared sensitive film.

2. It was hoped that differences would appear which would make it possible to distinguish hardwoods from softwoods, and deciduous trees from evergreens.

3. It was also hoped that differences in chlorophyll content could be determined from the photographs.

4. However, no obvious differences appeared in the photographs, all of which were about equally bright.

5. There is need for further research to determine the chlorophyll content of leaves.

Bibliography
[In the original report, a bibliography of sources was included.]

---

29 The Oral Report at a Science Congress

If you carry on scientific investigations, sooner or later you will find yourself face to face with an audience. This audience may consist of the fellow pupils of your science class or your friends in a science club. It may also be an audience of complete strangers at a science fair or a science congress. Whatever the case may be, there you are, standing before them (with your knees shaking), and it is up to you to get across to your listeners the essential features of your investigation. Obviously, it is important for you to know what to do and how to do it.

In order to know what to do, you must know what will be expected of you. It is necessary that you know the rules under which the science congress will be run. Essentially, you will be expected to tell the audience all about your investigation in such terms that everything is clearly understandable. In addition you will be expected to answer questions from the audience, or to defend your methods and conclusions against criticism. This means that the technique of making an oral report is quite different from that of making a written report. It may be true that the information you want to give and the ideas you want to explain are the same. The technique of presenting them, however, is quite different.

To begin with, don't fall into an error which is very common among scientists, including some very famous ones. Perhaps an exaggerated description of what happens at an imaginary meeting of a fictitious scientific society will point up this error.

Professor Hookbill has just succeeded in crossbreeding homing pigeons with parakeets to produce a new kind of bird which can ask somebody the way home when it gets lost. He is invited "to read a paper" about his work before the meeting of the Atlantis Parakeet Association. ("Reading a paper" is a common expression which means delivering an oral report.) Unfortunately, Professor

Hookbill takes the words literally. He has written a report of his work which he is going to submit for publication anyway, so he figures he will kill two birds with one stone. He will read the same paper to the audience, and then send it to the editor of the magazine. Now, while Professor Hookbill may be a world-famous authority on homing pigeons and parakeets, he doesn't happen to be a trained speaker. When he gets up to begin " reading his paper," the audience soon realizes what it is in for. He buries his nose in his papers, so that his voice cannot be heard beyond the first three rows. And that voice! It drones on in monotony as he reads off long lists of figures from tables, and minute details of technique. There is no expression in his reading. The audience, resigned to its fate but polite to the end, sits there bored and fidgety. The lucky ones fall asleep to the tune of his monotonous droning. After what seems like several centuries, Professor Hookbill stops, and there is a mild patter of applause out of politeness. The professor goes home, sure that he has made a wonderful speech which impressed his audience. The listeners, however, leave thinking what a waste of time the evening has been.

FIGURE **34.** *How would you plan an oral report?*

a. *Like this?*

Because the available instruments of measure were of such marked imperfection, as reflected by the margin of error obtained by statistical calculation, empirical evidence of gradations of reaction by the specimen of Rana pipiens . . . . blah, blah, blah . . . .

Although this is a make-believe description, it comes very close to the truth. Many a scientist literally "reads a paper" to the audience instead of giving a stimulating oral report. Too often the speaker forgets that he is an expert. He assumes that everyone knows just as much about the subject as he does, and that everyone is just as interested in it as he is. He assumes that the entire audience is hanging breathlessly on every statistic which he drops during his talk. Of course, these assumptions are all wrong; this is one reason why the average person may be either bored or mystified by scientific meetings.

So, don't make these mistakes. When you make your report to an audience, put a little drama into it. Make it interesting. Make the audience sit up and take notice (Figure 34-b). Even a bit of humor inserted at the right place makes your report more attractive. Above all, keep in mind the following question — "Would this report be clear to me if I knew only as much as the listener knows about the subject?"

Now that we know what to avoid, let's get down to cases. What should we do when giving an oral report on our investigation?

b. *Or like this?*

1. Know your audience. If you know what kind of people make up your audience, you start off with a big advantage. You don't want to talk over their heads, and yet you don't want to talk down to them. You don't want to confuse them by speaking in terms they don't understand, and yet you don't want to insult them by explaining things which they already know. If you are speaking to a school audience on a subject for which you have done a great deal of research, you had better assume that your audience knows nothing about it. Explain all the unusual terms and techniques which you mention in your report, even though it is possible that some of those present are familiar with them. If, however, you are speaking to a science congress, you should avoid insulting your audience with unnecessary explanations, when you are sure that everyone present is familiar with the subject of your report.

2. *Know your report* — *don't read it.* It is unlikely that you are a skilled actor — a Charles Laughton who can read a passage with such skill and expression that you can hold an audience spellbound. Therefore, you are better off if you do not attempt to *read* your report. Usually a report which is read sounds stiff and stilted. It is uninteresting. You will do much better if you know your material so well that it pours forth freely when you start talking.

This does not mean that you should write out a report and memorize it. Reciting a memorized report may be as bad or worse than reading it. You cannot afford to be tied to any papers or to any memorized words. You must feel free to direct all your attention to the audience. Of course, you may want to have at hand some cards with an outline of the topics you want to cover. A single look at each card, however, should tell you what you want to talk about, and then you should be able to speak freely. There is one exception to this. If you are quoting directly, it is a good idea to have the quotation written on a card so that you can read it exactly, word for word.

Whatever you do, remember that you are speaking to an audience. Every person in that audience is entitled to know what you are talking about, so speak loudly enough to be heard by all. Remember, also, that if it is worth saying at all, it is worth saying in good English. Two more points — if you want to *capture* the attention of your audience, you must be forceful and dramatic, and if you want to *hold* attention, you must make your report understandable and interesting.

3. Know exactly what you want to say. Putting into words precisely what you mean to say requires first that you yourself be clear in your mind. You must know exactly what you want to get across. You cannot stand up before your audience and say, "I know what I mean, but I cannot express it." This is an immediate confession of confusion in your mind. You *must* know how to say it if you intend to tell it to someone else. Therefore, in preparing your report, you must analyze all the material which you collected during your research. You must select from the total mass of material that which will be most important and most interesting to the audience. You cannot possibly include everything. Be as selective as you can, and then organize the selected material so that it makes good sense.

4. Present your report in an organized fashion. A good oral report must be as well organized as a good written report. You cannot just begin to talk in the middle of nowhere. Everything must be planned so that the total report makes good, logical sense. Perhaps the report should begin with an introduction which points out how it relates to the general subject of the science congress being held. Perhaps the introduction might tell how you came to select this subject, and give a little history of your previous work. In any case, there should be an introduction.

Your introduction should include a clear statement of the problem, and it should lead logically into the body of the report. Here you tell what you did and what happened. It is desirable to support your statements with evidence and data, but limit the data to what is really essential. Evidence and data should be offered in the form of slides, charts, or other illustrative material. Some suggestions about this kind of material will be found later on in this chapter.

After you have presented the body of the report, you should explain how these results led you to a conclusion. State your conclusion simply and clearly for all to hear. Now point out any applications which your findings may have, and then summarize the essential ideas which you want to leave with your audience.

5. Use visual materials. Getting an idea across to an audience is a teaching job, and *you* are the teacher. Therefore, you should bring into play every technique and device which a teacher uses in teaching his class. Or better still, think of an advertiser on television. He is selling a product. What are some of the tricks he uses to catch your attention and focus it on his product? Naturally you cannot use all his methods. You cannot put on a show, but you can borrow a few of his tricks. Notice that he not only talks about his product, but he also shows it. He calls your attention to pictures which illustrate what his product does, and often these pictures or models have moving parts to catch and hold attention.

Speaking to an audience appeals only to their auditory sense, the sense of hearing. Your talk will be more effective if, like the advertiser, you can also appeal to other senses at the same time. This is where visual aids come into play. You want to reach as many senses as possible, but it is easiest to appeal to the visual, the sense of sight.

What kind of visual aids you will use must of necessity depend on the subject matter of your report, and on the nature of the science congress, or other place at which the report is to be given. But there are two obvious rules to keep in mind regardless of the subject or the place: your visual aids must be large enough to be seen by everyone; and they must be attractive and understandable.

For example, if your project involves the construction of a working model of some piece of apparatus, the ideal visual aid would be the actual model you made. You could demonstrate to the audience just exactly how the model works. If this is a science fair, where the audience can get very close to your model, a small model is satisfactory. It might even be desirable to rig it in such a way that the visitors themselves can operate it. Yet if you do this, there is the risk of damage, and therefore you must protect the model in some way. Perhaps the model can be put in a transparent case of some kind, with a button to push or a lever to pull for those who want to make it work. Many modern museums rig their demonstrations in this way; they find that setups " inviting " the visitor to do something are extremely popular. However, if your audience is seated in a large auditorium, and the model is small, nobody will see the demonstration so it serves no useful purpose. Under the circumstances it would be better to use some other form of demonstration.

If you happen to be making your report in a classroom, there is sure to be blackboard space available. Don't hesitate to use it. Put on the blackboard in advance, if you have the time, the problem you are going to consider, or any new terms which will be used, or diagrams to which you intend to refer while you talk. Be sure that your writing is large, clear, and neat; and make sure that the diagrams are attractive. Use colored chalk rather than white chalk.

Draw with the flat side of the chalk instead of the point to get broader lines which are more clearly visible. If you are a good artist, you can actually build up your diagram dynamically while you are talking, but if your drawing skills are limited, you had better draw the whole thing in advance. Better still, get an artistic friend to do it for you if this is possible. The idea is to make the blackboard look as attractive as possible when the audience comes in. Don't forget to refer to the material on the board at the right moment. Don't refer to it from a distance. Walk up to the blackboard and use a pointer to indicate what you are talking about.

If no blackboard is available, you must depend on other media. For example, the room may be equipped with a lantern slide projector. You can make excellent slides very easily and quickly by writing or drawing with pencil, crayons, or transparent inks on *ground glass*. Ask your adviser to tell you more about this. But before you take the time to make slides, find out for certain whether a projector will be available. Also, test your slides without an audience. You can feel pretty foolish if you put a slide on for an audience, and it does not show up well.

If projection facilities are lacking, you will have to prepare charts and diagrams on cardboards or oaktag sheets. Whatever was said for diagrams on the board goes equally well for such charts. Remember — color is more effective than black and white. Charts are most effective when they are large, simple, clear, and attractive. You had better try to find out where you will be able to hang your charts, because if there is no provision for hanging them, you will have to figure out another way of showing them to the audience. Make sure that you refer to the charts and that you point out the essential things at the right moment.

Even better than charts or slides are three-dimensional models, which must be large and clear. Graphs can also be given a three-dimensional look.

Best of all, it may be possible for you to demonstrate an actual technique right in front of the audience. Or you may be able to show the very animals which made up your experimental and control groups.

6. Watch your time. You probably know how important timing is on a radio program. Well, it is just as important to you in making your report. It is essential for you to know how much time you will be allowed for the total report so that you can properly allot time for each part. For example, if you are allotted ten minutes, you can't afford to take eight minutes for the introduction because then you will have only two minutes for everything else. But if you have thirty minutes, you may want to spend eight minutes on the introduction. Tailor your report to fit the time. Don't try to squeeze in too much detail. Get the major ideas across. You may be able to mention some of the details later on, for instance, in reply to a question.

7. Give credit where credit is due. Don't let your audience get the impression that you are claiming credit for something which was done by someone else. Give credit for help in materials and ideas. Explain clearly what work you yourself did and what you found out by reading about the work of others.

8. Admit any weaknesses in your report. Don't try to cover up possible sources of error or flaws in your report. Admit them. Point them out yourself. Tell the audience that your conclusions are stated within certain limitations of which you are well aware. If you don't do this yourself, someone in the audience is sure to throw them up at you during the discussion period. You can steal their thunder by telling the audience ahead of time that you are aware of the faults in your work.

9. Accept criticism gracefully. No doubt someone in the audience will criticize something that you did or said. Accept all criticism gracefully and politely. This does not mean that you necessarily agree with the criticism, but merely that this is neither the time nor the place to make an issue of it. If you really think the criticism is valid, accept it, thank the person who made it, and admit that he is right. On the other hand, if you do not agree with the criticism, thank the person anyway, but say that you do not think his criticism is valid. If it is possible to state very briefly why you do not accept the criticism, then do so, but if it will take too long to explain, invite the person to discuss it with you at another time. Don't, however, get into an argument over it.

10. Answer questions honestly and squarely. The question period can be a very trying part of a science congress. This is the time when the audience can " get even with " the speaker. At worst, the audience can literally tear the speaker apart. You must be prepared for questions, and you must answer each question briefly, politely, and honestly. Since a question is frequently asked in such a way that the audience cannot hear it, you should repeat the question out loud before you begin your answer.

There is absolutely nothing wrong with saying, " I don't know. This is something which is worth finding out." You are better off admitting that you don't know the answer than you are trying to bluff your way through. Bluffing is almost sure to boomerang on you.

Frequently a question is asked which is not related to the subject of your report. If this happens, it is wise to point out politely that the question is off the subject, and that you would prefer not to answer it at the moment. Be polite. Try not to give the questioner the feeling that he is being brushed aside, but at the same time, keep to the subject at hand.

During the question period somebody is sure to ask the question, " What good is your idea? What are its practical applications? " Don't let this question throw you. Be prepared to answer it.

Of course, you may be able to rattle off a list of practical applications which will satisfy the questioner. But even if you know of no practical applications for your idea, this does not spoil it as an idea. Just remember that pure science is the study of science for the sake of knowledge alone — not for the practical applications which may grow out of it. When a new idea emerges, it is likely that the only person in the whole world who believes it is the author.

Many years ago, Michael Faraday gave a classic answer when asked by a very important person who was visiting his laboratory, " Of what use is your discovery? " His reply was brief and to the point. " Of what use is a newborn child? " he asked. The V.I.P. had nothing further to say.

Now to sum up. Making an oral report does not mean " reading a paper." It means telling a live audience the most important things that you have accomplished. It means telling the story in a lively, dramatic, interesting way, supported by attractive and effective illustrative material. It means answering questions honestly, and accepting criticism gracefully.

One of the best ways to prepare for your report is to have a practice session. Ask your teacher for permission to present your report to a science class. Present it exactly as you expect to do it at the science congress, using all the illustrative material you intend to use there. Then listen to the criticism of your classmates, go home and think them over. If any of your plans require changing, you can still make the changes before the main event.

30 Conclusion

Here you are; you have carried on a scientific investigation. It wasn't too bad, was it? Perhaps this will be the first in a long series of investigations. Perhaps you will like this kind of work so well that you will consider the field of science as a career. Have you thought of science in this way?

We live in an age of scientific wonders. The miracles which we take for granted in our everyday life were developed as the result of scientific investigations. First came the "pure" scientists, asking questions about nature and evolving basic principles to describe, as correctly as possible, natural phenomena. Often these basic discoveries seemed to have no practical use. Inevitably, however, the abstract scientific principle is examined by the "applied" scientists — the engineers, the mechanics, and the technicians who seek to put principles to work. Ultimately a use is found — a use which makes human life better or easier; a use which provides the world with new things and new devices; a use which was never imagined to be possible.

Who would have dared to dream, one hundred years ago, that a play enacted somewhere on a stage could be seen and heard a thousand miles away merely by turning a few knobs on a small box in the living room? "Impossible!" "Witchcraft!" Yet this is as commonplace as cooking in our modern life. And television is only in its infancy.

Who would have believed, one hundred years ago, that man could circle the globe in a matter of hours by hurtling through the air in a machine weighing several tons? Certainly this seemed impossible when the Wright brothers flew their craft for a few yards not so long ago. Yet, we already have planes which fly faster than sound, and they get faster every day.

Who would have dreamed, one hundred years ago, that a surgeon could repair a human heart? "An injury to the heart is death

Each new discovery in science creates a demand for many more scientists.
Have you thought about a future for yourself in science — as a teacher,
technician, engineer, or research worker?

itself! " it was said. Yet, not only have human hearts been repaired, but the heart and other organs have been replaced temporarily by mechanical devices — artificial hearts, artificial lungs, artificial kidneys. Who knows where this will lead?

Who would have thought possible a machine which can do in a fraction of a minute a complicated mathematical computation which would take a man hours, or days, or even years to complete? Mechanical brains? Machines that " remember "? " Fantastic! " " Impossible! " But they are here today.

Yes, science has made progress — amazing progress — in the last hundred years. And there is no end in sight. Rather, progress is speeding up. Each new discovery is the basis for not one but dozens of other developments. Scientific progress spreads and spreads without limit. As it spreads, it mushrooms and grows in scope, and the need for scientists becomes greater and greater.

We are now standing on the threshold of new wonders. We are reaching into the mysteries of the atom to extract power in such fantastic quantities that it staggers the imagination. We are sitting on the verge of space travel, long a matter of fiction and fantasy. Already we hear of man-made satellites; and rockets that penetrate the ionosphere.

We are beginning to probe into the mysteries of the human mind. We hear vague rumblings about the amazing possibilities of ESP (extrasensory perception), of telepathy, of mind over matter. We are finding newer and better ways to combat and destroy the germs and microbes which have harassed man ever since he has existed on the earth. Already we have animals which were born and raised in a completely germ-free environment. Will man be next?

Who can say what advances the next hundred years will bring? Who can say what improvements man will be able to make in his environment, or even in himself? Perhaps scientists will, to a far greater extent, turn their skills and methods toward the serious task of solving social problems.

You cannot predict what changes will occur, *but you can be part of it all.* You cannot say what changes the next hundred years will bring, *but you can help bring these changes about.* You can do these things if you make science your interest, your business, your career. The need for scientists is great beyond measure. Will *you* help fill this need? The progress of the world depends on scientists. Will *you* be playing your part in the process of remaking the world? It is for you to decide.

INFORMATION FOR FURTHER REFERENCE

Section A The Fundamentals of Statistics

Chapter 23 dealt with analyzing the data which you collected in your investigation. It was pointed out that the *raw* data which you collected must be properly organized and analyzed if it is to be made useful and meaningful. This appendix is provided to help you do exactly that.

1. Measures of central tendency

In drawing conclusions for your experiment, it is often necessary to find "a general rule," or to determine what is true in most cases. Of course, one way of doing this is to look at the data and make a guess. You can look at the figures and then say something like this: "On the whole, each trial took about fourteen seconds," or "Generally speaking, the animals weigh about 360 grams each." But such guesses are not accurate, and therefore they are not suitable for scientific work. It is much better to use a statistical method of finding the average. There are several different kinds of statistical averages, each of which has its own use. You should become acquainted with at least three of these: the arithmetic mean, the median, and the mode.

a. *The arithmetic mean.* This is the statistician's name for what most people call "the average." It is the most commonly used form of average, and it is very useful in analyzing data. Everybody knows how to find the average. All you do is add up all the separate weights, or the separate marks, or the separate ages, and then divide the total by the number of cases studied. Thus, for example, in Chapter 23, a case was cited in which a pupil had fifteen quiz marks — 9, 8, 10, 7, 6, 10, 10, 10, 9, 7, 10, 9, 9, 8, 10. Adding these fifteen grades gives a total of 132, and dividing this total by 15 gives 8.8 as the average. We can now say that *the arithmetic mean* (average mark) is 8.8. Notice that on not a single test did the pupil get 8.8 as a mark. However, generally speaking, 8.8 was his average mark. In much the same way, one of the tables in Chapter 21 gives the weights of five rats as 48, 51, 50, 49, and 53 grams respectively. Adding these figures gives a total of 251 grams, and dividing by 5 gives an arithmetic mean (average weight) of 50.2 grams. Again, note that not a single rat of the group actually weighs 50.2 grams. But they all weigh somewhere around that figure. So you see, the arithmetic mean gives a general picture of a group, but tells nothing about any individual in the group.

While the mean, as the arithmetic mean is often called, may be an extremely useful tool in analysis, it can be very misleading at times. Therefore, when you use a mean or average in your analysis, you must be careful that you are using it properly. Consider, for example, the following case. A posse is chasing a "bad hombre," and in the chase many shots are fired at him. One shot goes exactly one inch to the right of the villain's head, a second goes one inch to the left of his head, and a third goes one inch above his head. What is the "average" location of these three shots? Why — exactly in the middle of the bad man's head! "On the average" he is dead — shot right through the head. But still he goes riding madly along, unharmed by the "average" bullet. As in this case, "averages" do not always strike the mark. Therefore, they are not always appropriate.

Consider another situation. Suppose you are asked to determine the average yearly income of a group of ten men. It's quite simple. You find out the annual income of each man, and you tabulate the data as follows:

No. 1 — $2,000	No. 6 — $4,000
No. 2 — $2,500	No. 7 — $2,500
No. 3 — $2,500	No. 8 — $3,500
No. 4 — $5,000	No. 9 — $5,000
No. 5 — $3,000	No. 10 — $1,000,000

The total is $1,030,000, and dividing by 10 gives a mean (average income) of $103,000 per year. Now it seems fairly obvious that $103,000 per year is far from a true picture of the average income of the members of this group, even though the arithmetic is correct. Because the mean does not always give a "true" picture of the average, we often make use of a different kind of measure.

b. *The median.* The median is the middle member of a group. It is a sort of "average," too. For example, if there are five boys standing in line according to their respective heights, the third boy in line would represent the median height of the group, because

FIGURE **35.** *Comparison of Five Boys by Height to Show the Median Height*

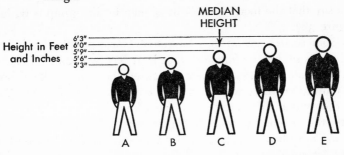

there are just as many boys shorter than this height as there are boys taller than this height (Figure 35).

In the same way, if we consider again the five rats whose mean weight was 50.2 grams, we find that the weights ran 48, 51, 50, 49, and 53 grams. When these weights are rearranged in order, the series becomes 48, 49, 50, 51, 53, and we can see at once that the median (middle) weight is 50 grams. There are just as many rats in the group which are heavier than 50 grams as there are rats which are lighter than 50 grams.

If the group being considered has an odd number of cases, the median is easy to find. But what happens if there is an even number? Let us consider the ten men whose annual salaries were discussed a few paragraphs back. We arrange the incomes in order, and the series becomes $2,000; $2,500; $2,500; $2,500; $3,000; $3,500; $4,000; $5,000; $5,000; $1,000,000. The median or mid-point is halfway between $3,000 and $3,500. We are safe in saying that the median annual salary of this group is $3,250. You can see at once that this gives a much truer picture of the salary situation in this group than is given by the mean of $103,000 per year.

c. *The mode.* The mode is a third kind of "average." It represents that characteristic which occurs more frequently in your group than any other kind. Perhaps it may be said to be the most typical case in the group — what is "in style" — what is "the mode." For example, suppose we open a piggy bank into which we have been dropping coins for a long time. We arrange the coins according to kind, and we find 25 pennies, 72 nickels, 36 dimes, 12 quarters, and 2 half dollars. In this case, the largest group is made up of nickels. There are more nickels than any other kind of coin. So we say that in this group, the nickel is *the mode.*

Or, imagine that we measure the heights of fifty men and we find that more men measure 68 inches than any other height. We can then say that the mode for height of men in this group is 68 inches (Figure 36).

Sometimes a group may have two "most popular kinds." Such a group is said to be *bimodal;* that is, it has two modes. For example, a certain investigator once measured the sperm cells of horses. He found that there were two most common sizes. This led him to the theory that there are two different kinds of sperms, those which carry the X chromosome and therefore are female determining sperms, and those which carry the Y chromosome and therefore are male determining.

FIGURE **36.** *Comparison of Fifty Men by Height to Show the Mode*

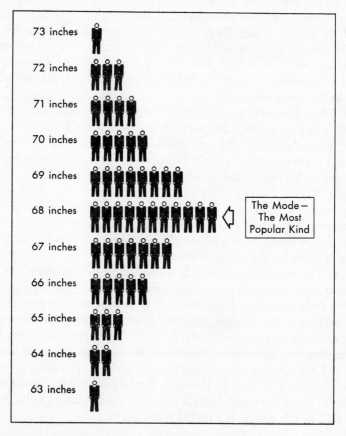

To summarize, there are three commonly used measures of central tendency — the arithmetic mean, the median, and the mode. They are all *measures of central tendency,* and each has its own uses. But as you will see in a moment, a mean, median, or mode by itself can be a misleading figure. Together with the average, you must determine how far the members of the group spread from the center, and this takes us to *measures of variability.*

2. Measures of variability

In a certain experiment two subjects (A and B) were asked to perform 20 tasks of equal difficulty. Figure 37 is a record of the time (in seconds) needed for each task. Which subject gave a better performance? If you take the average (mean), you will find that the two subjects had exactly the same average — 6 seconds. Yet there is quite a difference between the two sets of scores. Subject B was

FIGURE **37.** *Comparison of Performance of Twenty Tasks of Equal Difficulty by Two Subjects*

TASK NO.	TIME IN SECONDS REQUIRED TO COMPLETE TASK	
	Subject A	Subject B
1	8	6
2	7	4
3	3	5
4	6	5
5	2	8
6	6	6
7	7	6
8	5	6
9	5	7
10	4	6
11	5	6
12	7	6
13	10	6
14	8	6
15	6	7
16	6	6
17	5	5
18	4	6
19	9	6
20	7	7

FIGURE **38.** *Comparison of Four Groups of Fifty People by Height*

HEIGHT IN INCHES	GROUP 1	GROUP 2	GROUP 3	GROUP 4
78	/	/	//	/
76	/	/	///	卌
74	//	/	卌	卌 卌 //
72	////	/	卌	卌
70	卌 //	//	卌 /	//
68	卌 卌 卌 卌 ///	///	卌 ///	/
66	卌 //	卌 卌 卌	卌 /	卌
64	////	卌 卌	卌	卌 卌 //
62	//	卌 ///	卌	卌
60	/	卌	///	/
58	/	///	//	/
2				
0				
	TOTAL = 50	TOTAL = 50	TOTAL = 50	TOTAL = 50

more consistent than A. His time did not vary much on the different tasks, hovering between 5 and 7 seconds nearly all the time. Subject A was quite inconsistent. He completed one task in a record time of 2 seconds, but on other tests he dragged on for 9 or 10 seconds. Obviously, the average of 6 seconds does not tell the whole story. To make the average more meaningful, it is always necessary to qualify it by adding some indication of how consistent this figure is. We call these qualifiers *measures of variability,* and we will consider three of them: *the range, the average deviation,* and *the standard deviation.*

a. *The range.* The range is the spread of scores from the lowest to the highest. Thus, the scores of subject A spread from a low of 2 to a high of 10 (a range of 9 seconds), while for subject B the scores spread from a low of 4 to a high of 8 (a range of 5 seconds). Now we can better describe the two subjects of our experiment. We can say that subject A has an average time of 6 seconds with scores ranging from 2 to 10 seconds, and subject B has the same average with scores ranging from 4 to 8 seconds. Certainly this is a better description of the two subjects than merely stating the average.

Still, the *range* is not a very good measure of variability, because it does not tell how the scores scatter in between the two extremes. Study Figure 38. It gives the heights in inches of four different groups of people. Note that the *range* is exactly the same in each of the four groups. Yet the distribution is quite different. Because the range fails to give a satisfactory picture of a distribution, we usually make use of the other measures of variability which will now be described.

b. *The average deviation.* Did you ever look at a target? Figure 39 is a picture of the kind of target which might be used for pistol shooting. Obviously a shot in the bull's-eye should get the highest score, and a shot near the bull's-eye a better score than a shot farther away from the bull's-eye. It doesn't matter whether a shot is above, below, to the right, or to the left of the bull's-eye. What is important is the distance of the shot from the bull's-eye.

Suppose you wanted to compare the target shooting ability of two boys. You could let each boy take five shots, and then you could measure how many inches from the bull's-eye each shot hit. Next, you could take the average of the deviations from the bull's-eye for each boy, and in this way reach a single measure of accuracy, which could be called the *average deviation.* Thus, for example, suppose the shots fired by the two boys were summarized as in Figure 40.

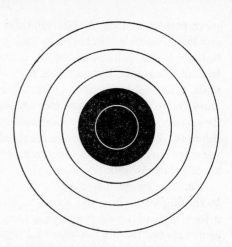

FIGURE **39.**
On this 25-foot target for pistol firing, no printed score values appear in the rings. How could a series of scores for two people be compared for marksmanship?

FIGURE **40.** *Summary of Shots Fired into Target by Each of Two Boys*

	INCHES FROM CENTER OF TARGET	
SHOT NO.	*Boy No. 1*	*Boy No. 2*
1	4	2
2	8	1
3	3	7
4	6	8
5	9	2
TOTAL DEVIATION	30	20
AVERAGE DEVIATION	$^{30}/_5 = 6$	$^{20}/_5 = 4$

It seems quite reasonable to say that boy number 2 is a better shot than boy number 1, because his shots clustered closer to the bull's-eye. To put it another way, the *average deviation* of his shots from the bull's-eye was less.

Let us now return to the two subjects with whose scores the section on variability was opened (Figure 37). You will remember that they each had an average score of 6, but that we judged subject B to be the more consistent of the two. However, exactly how much more consistent is he? To answer this question, we can use the same system that we used to determine which boy was a better shot. If we consider the mean of the test marks to be the "bull's-eye," we can measure the average deviation of each student from his " bull's-eye." Just as in the case of the target, the average deviation told us how close around the bull's-eye the shots clustered, so in this case, the average deviation will tell us how close around the mean the test marks clustered. To find the *average deviation from the mean,* we take each mark separately, and determine how far it is away from the mean. Then we add up all the separate deviations and divide by 20, the number of tests involved (Figure 41).

Now we can say that *subject A had an average score of 6 seconds plus or minus an average deviation of 1.5 seconds.* This can be written briefly as 6 sec. ± 1.5 (mean ± A.D.). Actually this indicates that somewhat more than 50 per cent of the time, subject A took between 4.5 and 7.5 seconds to complete a task. In the same way *subject B had an average score of 6 seconds ± 0.5 seconds,* indicating that more than 50 per cent of the time he took somewhere between 5.5 and 6.5 seconds to complete a task. By comparing the figures for A (6 sec. ± 1.5) and for B (6 sec. ± 0.5), we can come to a better conclusion about the variability of the two subjects. Subject B was much more consistent; he showed much less variability in his scores.

c. *The standard deviation.* Average deviation has the fault of considering all deviations as equally important, no matter how far from the average they may be. But for many reasons, it is desirable to give heavier weighting to those deviations which fall further from the average, because these are actually larger errors. To give weight to errors according to their seriousness — their increasing distance from the mean — we use *the standard deviation* as the measure of variability. (Standard deviation is usually represented by the Greek letter *sigma,* written σ.)

In calculating the standard deviation, we first determine each individual deviation, as we did before. *But this time we square each deviation* (multiply it by itself). Thus, if the score deviates from the average by 2, we multiply 2 by itself and write down 4. If the score deviates by 5, we multiply 5 by itself and write down 25. Now we add up all the squared deviations, and we find their average by dividing by the number of scores. Lastly, we take the square root of the result, and this gives us the standard deviation. A formula for this might be written in the following way:

$$\sigma = \sqrt{\frac{\text{sum of squared deviations}}{\text{number of cases}}}$$

SUBJECT A		READ IN DIRECTION OF ARROWS ↓	SUBJECT B	
AVERAGE TIME (MEAN) = 6 SEC.			AVERAGE TIME (MEAN) = 6 SEC.	
Deviation from mean	*Time in seconds*	*Test No.*	*Time in seconds*	*Deviation from mean*
2	8	← 1 →	6	0
1	7	2	4	2
3	3	3	5	1
0	6	4	5	1
4	2	5	8	2
0	6	6	6	0
1	7	7	6	0
1	5	8	6	0
1	5	9	7	1
2	4	10	6	0
1	5	11	6	0
1	7	12	6	0
4	10	13	6	0
2	8	14	6	0
0	6	15	7	1
0	6	16	6	0
1	5	17	5	1
2	4	18	6	0
3	9	19	6	0
1	7	20	7	1
30		← TOTAL DEVIATION →		10
$\frac{30}{20}$ = 1.5		← AVERAGE DEVIATION →		$\frac{10}{20}$ = 0.5
6 SEC. ± 1.5 SEC.		M ± A.D.	6 SEC. ± 0.5 SEC.	

In the case of our previous subjects A and B, we can calculate the standard deviation of their scores on the 20 tasks as follows:

For Subject A:

Deviations from mean — See Figure 41.

Squared deviations from mean = 4, 1, 9, 0, 16, 0, 1, 1, 1, 4,
$$1, 1, 16, 4, 0, 0, 1, 4, 9, 1$$

Sum of squared deviations from mean = 74

$$\sigma = \sqrt{\tfrac{74}{20}} = \sqrt{3.7} = 1.92$$

For Subject B:

Deviations from mean — See Figure 41.

Squared deviations from mean = 0, 4, 1, 1, 4, 0, 0, 0, 1, 0,
$$0, 0, 0, 0, 1, 0, 1, 0, 0, 1$$

Sum of squared deviations from mean = 14

$$\sigma = \sqrt{\tfrac{14}{20}} = \sqrt{.7} = 0.83$$

The mean $\pm$ σ usually includes about 2/3 of all the cases in a normal distribution. Of all the measures of variability, the standard deviation is the one most commonly used in scientific work.

3. Measures of correlation

In analyzing the results of your investigation, you may find it necessary to determine whether there is any relationship between two series of events, or between two sets of measurements. For example, you may want to know whether there is any relationship between the length and the width of a series of elm leaves. Or, perhaps you want to know whether the rate at which the heart of an animal beats is in any way related to the size of the animal. Or you want to know if there is any connection between batting ability and fielding ability in baseball; or between batting ability in baseball and goal shooting ability for free throws in basketball. Such a relationship, if it exists, is known as a *correlation*.

The idea of correlation is quite commonplace. In everyday life we frequently look for relationships between two things. For example, we may say that " alcohol and gasoline do not mix." We are implying by this statement that driving while under the influence of liquor goes hand in hand with accidents. In the same way, when we use the expression " like father, like son," we are expressing the belief that there is a high degree of relationship between the traits of fathers and the traits of their children. And when we say that " a falling barometer indicates a storm," we show that we believe a high correlation exists between air pressure and weather conditions.

While such general statements as "smoking causes lung cancer" may be satisfactory as ordinary personal opinions, they are not good enough for science. In carrying out a scientific investigation, we must have a more accurate measure of relationship. It is not enough to say, for example, that "good batters in baseball make good goal shooters in basketball." A scientist would want to know whether such a relationship could actually be demonstrated. He would want a more accurate measuring stick of relationship. Such a yardstick is provided by the statistical measure called *the coefficient of correlation.*

In order to understand what we mean by the coefficient of correlation, let us consider an example. Suppose we wanted to find out whether there is really any relationship between batting ability in baseball and goal shooting ability for free throws in basketball. For simplicity, suppose we consider 20 boys from our school and calculate the batting average and goal shooting average for free throws of each. We might set up a table and a scattergram, as in Figure 42, and discover that the best batter is also the best goal shooter, that the second best batter is the second best goal shooter, that the third best batter is the third best goal shooter, and so forth down the line. If our results came out this way, we could say that there is *a perfect and positive relationship* between batting ability and goal shooting ability. In statistical terms, we would describe this as *a perfect positive correlation,* or a correlation of +1.

However, we might discover that the best batter is the *poorest* goal shooter, the second best batter is the second poorest goal shooter, the third best batter is the third poorest goal shooter, and so forth. The poorest batter would then be the best goal shooter (Figure 43). In this case, *there is still a perfect relationship* between batting ability and goal shooting ability, but it is certainly not a positive relationship. On the contrary, *it is a reverse, or negative, relationship.* In statistical terms, this would be described as *a perfect negative correlation,* or a correlation of −1.

Probably we would find a result different from that in either of the two foregoing cases. Many good batters might turn out to be good goal shooters, while a few would turn out to be poor goal shooters. The table and scattergram in this case (Figure 44) might not seem at first glance to show any obvious relationship between the two abilities. But look again at the scattergram. Place the tips of

FIGURE **42.** *Theoretical Comparison of Baseball Batting Average with Goal Shooting Average for Basketball Free Throws for Each of Twenty Boys*

BOY	BATTING AVERAGE	GOAL SHOOTING AVERAGE	BOY	BATTING AVERAGE	GOAL SHOOTING AVERAGE
A	.200	.600	K	.300	.700
B	.210	.610	L	.310	.710
C	.220	.620	M	.320	.720
D	.230	.630	N	.330	.730
E	.240	.640	O	.340	.740
F	.250	.650	P	.350	.750
G	.260	.660	Q	.360	.760
H	.270	.670	R	.370	.770
I	.280	.680	S	.380	.780
J	.290	.690	T	.390	.790

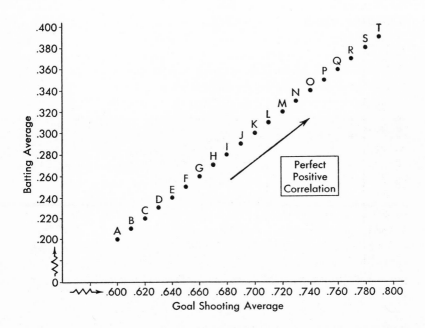

FIGURE **43.** *A Second Theoretical Comparison of Baseball Batting Average with Goal Shooting Average for Basketball Free Throws for Each of Twenty Boys*

BOY	BATTING AVERAGE	GOAL SHOOTING AVERAGE	BOY	BATTING AVERAGE	GOAL SHOOTING AVERAGE
A	.390	.600	K	.290	.700
B	.380	.610	L	.280	.710
C	.370	.620	M	.270	.720
D	.360	.630	N	.260	.730
E	.350	.640	O	.250	.740
F	.340	.650	P	.240	.750
G	.330	.660	Q	.230	.760
H	.320	.670	R	.220	.770
I	.310	.680	S	.210	.780
J	.300	.690	T	.200	.790

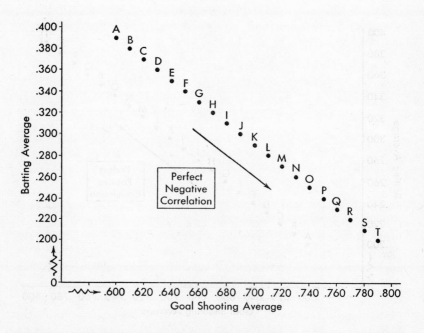

your forefingers over points *A* and *R* to hide these two isolated cases. Now do you see the relationship? It is somewhat rough, but it indicates a flow upward and to the right; i.e., *some* positive correlation. The positive correlation isn't perfect, but it does exist to a marked degree.

If the cases on a scattergram should turn out to be scattered evenly over the entire graph — top left, top right, center, lower left, lower right — then obviously there would be *no* relationship at all between the two characteristics being studied. In this event, we would say that there is *no correlation, or that the correlation is zero.*

So you see, the correlation between two things may range from perfect and positive (+1) all the way to perfect and negative (−1). Of course, there can be any degree of correlation between +1 and −1, including no correlation at all (zero). In statistical terms the correlation between two sets of data is expressed numerically as a *coefficient of correlation,* which lies somewhere along the scale in Figure 45.

There are several ways of determining the correlation between two sets of data. The scatter diagram (as used in Figures 42, 43, and 44) can be used to get a rough idea of the correlation, but to determine it more accurately mathematical formulas must be used. Two of the most commonly used methods of finding the coefficient of correlation are:

a. Spearman's " rank-difference " method, in which the relative ranks of the two sets of measurements are compared.
b. Pearson's " product-moment " method, in which the deviation from the average of each series is considered.

Of these two methods, Pearson's is the one used most commonly in scientific work. However, the Spearman method may be easier to use where only a small number of cases is involved. We cannot take the space in this book to show how these methods are actually used in determining the coefficient of correlation; any standard book on statistics will explain the methods of working it out. For our purposes, it is enough to understand the general meaning of correlation.

Before we leave correlation, one word of caution must be added. *The fact that a high statistical correlation exists between two things does not necessarily mean that the two items are actually related.* To illustrate this important fact, a statistician once showed (with tongue in cheek) that the amount of money spent by the British Navy had a high correlation with the number of bananas

FIGURE **44.** *A Third Theoretical Comparison of Baseball Batting Average with Goal Shooting Average for Basketball Free Throws for Each of Twenty Boys*

BOY	BATTING AVERAGE	GOAL SHOOTING AVERAGE	BOY	BATTING AVERAGE	GOAL SHOOTING AVERAGE
A	.200	.720	K	.300	.700
B	.210	.630	L	.310	.750
C	.220	.600	M	.320	.760
D	.230	.640	N	.330	.790
E	.240	.670	O	.340	.680
F	.250	.610	P	.350	.740
G	.260	.660	Q	.360	.770
H	.270	.620	R	.370	.650
I	.280	.690	S	.380	.730
J	.290	.710	T	.390	.780

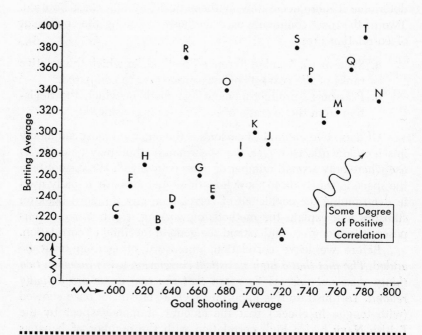

consumed by the British people. Obviously, there is no connection between these two things. So, remember that *the coefficient of correlation is only a number*. It indicates a degree of *statistical* relationship. It may not indicate any *actual* relationship. Certainly, it never demonstrates that one event is the cause of another.

FIGURE **45.** *Scale of Values for Coefficient of Correlation*

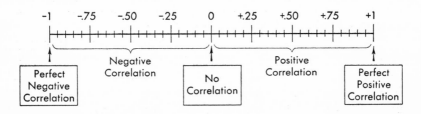

4. Measures of reliability

When a statistician speaks of the results of statistical measurement as *reliable*, he is talking about the likelihood of getting the same results if the same measurement is made again, or if the same experiment is carried out again, or if another comparable group is studied under the same conditions. He needs a way to determine reliability because he wants to know if there is an even chance that the same result will occur again and again, or if the odds in favor of or against it occurring again are 2 to 1, 100 to 1, 1,000 to 1, or 50,000 to 1. In other words, he is applying the "law of chance" to his results to see if they are trustworthy.

Statistical reliability depends on two major factors — the number of cases used for a study, and the variation among them. Let us see why this is so. Suppose you are studying the effect of a certain diet on the weight of white rats. There are only *five* white rats in your experimental group. At the same time, a scientist carrying on a similar experiment uses a group of *five hundred* rats. In all likelihood, his results can better predict the effect of this diet *on white rats in general* than your results can. For this reason, we say that his results are *more reliable* than yours. His chances of predicting correctly are better than yours because his prediction is based on more cases. Therefore, we can say, *the greater the number of cases used, the more reliable your result is likely to be.*

However, the variability of the cases enters into the picture, too. Suppose you are comparing the effect of two different diets on white rats, and you are using the same number of rats in each part of your experiment. After a while, you find that with Diet A each rat has gained between 30 and 40 grams in weight, while with Diet B each rat has gained anywhere from 10 to 60 grams. The gains on Diet B were much more variable than those on Diet A. Certainly, if you feed the same diets to new groups of rats, you can predict the result better for Diet A than for Diet B, because the result with Diet A is likely to vary less than the result with Diet B. Therefore, we can say, *the less the variation among the cases used, the more reliable your result is likely to be.*

Now that we understand what *reliability* means in a statistical sense, let us see how it is measured. There are two different measures of reliability which are commonly used — *probable error* (abbreviated P. E.) and *standard error* (represented by the Greek letter epsilon — ϵ). Let us consider them in that order.

a. *Probable error* (*P. E.*). Suppose you are preparing for a baseball game in a vacant lot, and you are laying out the bases. You know that the distance between home plate and first base should be 90 feet. So you decide where home plate is to be, and then you pace off 90 feet to locate first base. Simple enough — but wait a minute. How reliable was your measurement? If you paced it off again, would first base be in exactly the same place? Or would it be a little closer to home plate, or a little farther away?

Let us see how we can determine the reliability of such a measurement. Pace off what you think is 90 feet. Now take a tape measure, and measure the distance you laid out. Suppose it measures 92 feet. You are 2 feet over. Try again. This time suppose the distance measures 89 feet. You are one foot under. Try pacing off 90 feet one hundred different times. You will find that the distance you have marked off by pacing is sometimes a little more than 90 feet, and sometimes a little less. Now suppose you average up the errors, and you find that on the average you are off by about 2 feet.

You can conclude that when you pace off 90 feet, you are actually pacing off 90 feet *more* or *less*. But 50 per cent of the time, the distance you pace off should be within 2 feet of an accurately measured 90 feet. (The other 50 per cent of the time, your estimate may be over 92 feet or under 88 feet. This is because 2 feet is the *average error*, which means that you were wrong by more than 2 feet as often as you were wrong by less than 2 feet.) So, we can say that you have paced off 90 feet with a *probable error* of 2 feet. Another way of saying this is that you have a probable error of ±2.2

per cent of your estimate, since the probable error of 2 feet represents about 2.2 per cent of the total distance of 90 feet.

You will notice that in calculating the probable error, we did very much the same thing as we did in calculating the average deviation. Although the figure for both of these measures may be the same, the interpretation is quite different. Average deviation is used to describe only the variability of the group you are studying, whereas probable error is used to generalize about the whole population from which you have selected your sample group for detailed study.

Calculation of probable error usually is made by statistical formula rather than by repeated trials. For the proper way to compute probable error by formula, refer to a textbook on statistics.

b. *Standard error* (ϵ). In scientific work, the standard error (ϵ) is used more often than probable error to measure reliability. Standard error is about 1 1/2 times as large as probable error (or to say it in reverse, P. E. $= .67\ \epsilon$). Therefore, in the case cited above, for which you are pacing off 90 feet, the standard error is 3 feet. Whereas the probable error covers only about 50 per cent of the possibilities, the standard error covers two-thirds of the possibilities. Thus, the chances are 2 to 1 that the next time you pace it off, you will come within 3 feet of an accurate 90 feet. Just as probable error corresponds to average deviation, so standard error corresponds to standard deviation.

One way of calculating the standard error is to determine the probable error first, and then divide by .67. Thus, if P. E. $= 2$, $\epsilon = \frac{2}{.67} = 3$. Standard error usually is calculated by formula (as is probable error). For direct methods of calculating the standard error, refer to a textbook on statistics.

Before leaving this section on reliability, you should understand clearly what reliability does *not* mean.

1. Reliability does not mean accuracy. The fact that you have established that you can reliably pace off 90 feet does not mean that you cannot make mistakes. If, while you are pacing off the distance, you make an error in counting the paces, it may spoil this *particular* measurement; but it in no way changes the reliability that your measurements *in general* can have.

2. Reliability does not mean validity. We say a measure is valid if it measures that which it is supposed to measure. Suppose you plan to lay out the base paths for a baseball diamond, and then lay off four parallel lanes, each 90 feet in length. Your measurements may be very *reliable*, but they are *not valid* for baseball since you have laid out parallel paths instead of a diamond.

3. *Reliability does not mean truth.* Consider a very ridiculous case cited earlier: a cage with two feeding stations. Feeding station A is wired in such a way that an animal entering it gets a severe electric shock. Now put some fresh raw meat in feeding station A and Blanko dog biscuits in station B. Then you allow a dog to wander freely in the cage and choose the food he likes. You test five hundred dogs, and you reach the conclusion that dogs prefer Blanko dog biscuits to meat! Your result is statistically reliable because you used many cases and there was little variation. If the experiment were to be repeated *under the same conditions,* you could predict the result. But the conclusion is not true — for obvious reasons.

4. *Reliability does not mean representativeness.* We say a group is representative of the general population if it is a typical sample or cross section of the population as a whole. Now, suppose you are studying the heights of people, and you select ten thousand African pigmies as your subjects. Your results may be statistically reliable, yet they are not representative of people in general because the sample of the human race which you studied does not include a representative cross section of the entire human race.

This discussion of statistical measures has been brief, but it should cover your needs in testing and reporting the results of your scientific investigations. If you do need further clarification, refer to a textbook on statistics. Several good reference books on statistics are listed in the next section.

Section B Bibliography

1. Books on the History of Science.

An Illustrated History of Science, by Frank S. Taylor, Praeger, New York, 1955.   This book presents, in both text and pictures, the highlights of great events in the history of science. Many scenes from famous experiments are re-created in pictures.

Some Accidental Scientific Discoveries (no author given), Schaar & Co., Chicago (754 W. Lexington St.), 1955.   A fine pamphlet consisting of about 20 stories of accidental scientific discoveries. Some are famous incidents, while others are less widely known. Each story is documented by a bibliography of sources.

Main Currents of Scientific Thought, by Stephen F. Mason, Abelard-Schuman, New York, 1954.   A survey of biological and physical sciences through the ages.

A Short History of Science, by W. T. Sedgwick and H. W. Tyler, Macmillan, New York, 1939 (reissued in 1946).   This standard reference book provides a very useful survey of the developments in both the biological and physical sciences. It is especially good for pre-twentieth century science.

2. Books on the Meaning and Methods of Science.

What Is Science?, James R. Newman (editor), Simon & Schuster, New York, 1955.   This book contains articles by 12 eminent scientists and philosophers in which each man presents, for the benefit of the layman, a description of his field. The emphasis is on the nature of science and of scientific method.

Science, Servant of Man, by I. Bernard Cohen, Little, Brown, Boston, 1948.   This book describes the methods of science, their use in making scientific discoveries, and the applications of these discoveries to everyday life.

Science and Common Sense, by James B. Conant, Yale U. Press, New Haven, 1951.   A description of the methods used in science, and of techniques used in experimental work.

3. Classics of Science — Descriptions of Great Scientific Discoveries in the Words of the Discoverers.

A Half Century of Nobel Prize Winners (1901–1950). Three Volumes: *In Physics,* by Niels H. deV. Heathcote; *In Chemistry,* by Edward Farber; *In Medicine and Physiology,* by Lloyd G. Stevenson. Abelard-Schuman, New York, 1953. These three volumes make up an excellent set of source books. There is a brief biographic sketch of each Nobel Prize winner, followed by a description of the prize-winning work, usually in the words of the prize winner himself. Also given is a brief analysis of the consequences of the discovery.

The Motion of the Heart and Blood, by William Harvey (1628), Henry Regnery, Chicago, 1949. This is an English translation of the original description of the famous experiments which established the fact that blood circulates throughout the body.

Experiments in Plant Hybridization, by Gregor Mendel (1866), Harvard U. Press, Cambridge, Mass., 1948. This is an English translation of the original paper in which Mendel presented his famous experiments outlining the basic operation of the laws of heredity. It is simply and clearly written.

The Leeuwenhoek Letter, Barnett Cohen (translator), Society of American Bacteriologists, Baltimore, Md., 1937. This book contains a photographic copy of the original letter — dated Oct. 9, 1676 — in which Leeuwenhoek describes his discovery of protozoa. An English translation of the letter is also given.

Harvard Case Histories in Experimental Science, James B. Conant *et al.* (editors), Harvard U. Press, Cambridge, Mass., 1950–1954. Eight case histories have been published so far. Each case history is an analysis of original source work to show the development of a certain concept of science, such as No. 2 — *The Overthrow of the Phlogiston Theory,* or No. 6 — *Pasteur's Study of Fermentation.*

Classics of Science, reprinted in various issues of *Science News Letter.* In the 1920's and 1930's *Science News Letter* carried selected classics of science in the words of the authors (such as L. Spallanzani on *Regeneration in Earthworms,* or L. Agassiz on *Embryology of the Starfish*). These can be located by referring to the index for *Science News Letter* in a library which has a file for this periodical.

Great Experiments in Biology, by M. L. Gabriel and S. Fogel (editors), Prentice-Hall, Englewood Cliffs, N.J., 1955. This is an excellent source book, but it is written on the college level. It presents excerpts from the original research papers of great scientists — under various categories such as cell theory, physiology, microbiology, embryology, plant physiology, genetics, and evolution.

4. General References on How to Carry On an Investigation.

The Art of Scientific Investigation, by W. I. B. Beveridge, Norton, New York, 1951. This is a fine book, dealing mainly with research in biological fields, and written on the level of the research worker rather than that of a high school student. It contains many quotations by famous scientists, and describes many incidents in their lives.

The Principles of Scientific Research, by Paul Freedman, MacDonald, London, 1949. This book deals with the planning, organization, and conduct of scientific research. It is concisely and clearly written.

The Making of a Scientist, by A. Roe, Dodd, Mead, New York, 1953. A description of how a research study in psychology is conducted. The book also deals with the question of what leads people to enter the field of science as a life work.

Science in the Making, by Joel H. Hildebrand, Columbia U. Press, New York, 1957. The book is based on a series of lectures by the author, a chemist who became a distinguished research scientist. It deals with the methods used by scientists in their work, and it includes many examples from the author's own work.

5. Where to Get Ideas for Projects.

Thousands of Science Projects, compiled by M. E. Patterson and J. H. Kraus, National Science Foundation, Science Service, Washington, D.C. (1719 N. St., N.W.), 1953. This pamphlet lists a large number of projects under subject headings, using the Library of Congress system of classification. Each project was carried out at least once by a high school pupil.

Student Projects, compiled by John H. Woodburn, Future Scientists of America Foundation, National Science Teachers Association, Washington, D.C. (1201 16th St., N.W.), 1954. A pamphlet which classifies projects under 20 different types. Each type of project is illustrated by several examples of actual student projects. Two short student reports are given in full.

Scientific Instruments You Can Make, Helen M. Davis (editor), Science Clubs of America, Washington, D.C., 1954. This contains instructions by Science Talent Search winners for the building of many scientific instruments such as spectroscopes, tesla coils, stroboscopes, and computers. There are illustrations showing the completed instruments, and references to the use of these instruments in research in various fields.

Turtox Service Leaflets, General Biological Supply House, Chicago (8200 S. Hoyne Ave.), continuously revised. This is a series of 56 leaflets ranging from No. 1 — *How to Make an Insect Collection,* through No. 56 — *Simplified Photomicrography.* Each leaflet describes the techniques required for carrying out the particular activity suggested by the title.

The Book of Popular Science (ten volumes), The Grolier Society, New York, 1957. The material in this ten volume set, written on the level of junior and senior high school students, is in the form of articles on various subjects. Each volume is divided into 15 sections such as No. 1 — *The Universe,* and No. 8 — *Matter and Energy.* Section 15 is called *Projects and Experiments.*

Scientific American Reader, Simon & Schuster, New York, 1953. This book contains 67 articles reprinted from *Scientific American.* These articles are not always easy reading for a high school pupil, but in reading them, many ideas for projects will come to mind.

Scientific American, published monthly, Scientific American, Inc., New York (415 Madison Ave.). Every issue of *Scientific American* has a section called " The Amateur Scientist " in which some science activity is described. While these sections are not written primarily for junior or senior high school students, they can provide a plentiful source of ideas for projects.

Other magazines from which ideas for projects can be gleaned are *Popular Science Monthly, Popular Mechanics Magazine, Science and Mechanics,* and *Mechanix Illustrated.*

6. Where to Find the Techniques You Need for Your Project or Experiment.

Working with the Microscope, by Julian D. Corrington, McGraw-Hill, New York, 1941.   This book was written for the amateur microscopist. It suggests what to look at and how to go about it.

Some Simple Procedures in Sterile Technique and in the Handling of Bacteria, by Dorothy Pease, J. W. Edwards, Ann Arbor, Mich., 1951.   If your project involves the growing or handling of bacteria, you must learn something about sterile techniques. Here is an excellent manual for this purpose.

The Cultivation of Animal and Plant Cells, by Philip R. White, Ronald Press, New York, 1954.   An outstanding summary by an expert of basic methods used to grow tissue cells in vitro. It gives explicit instructions for the preparation of the materials, the nutrient solutions, methods of measuring growth, and applications.

Raising Small Animals for Pleasure and Profit, by Frank G. Ashbrook, D. Van Nostrand, Chicago, 1951.

A Practical Guide on the Care of Small Animals for Medical Research, by Harry G. Herrlein, Rockland Farms, New City, N.Y., 1949.

Home-Made Zoo, by S. S. Greenberg and E. L. Raskin, McKay, New York, 1952.
If your project involves living animals such as rabbits, rats, guinea pigs, hamsters, dogs, turtles, and snakes, you must know how to care for them, house them, feed them, and keep them safe from disease. These books will provide you with all the information you need to do a good job.

Plant Breeding for Everyone, by John Y. Beaty, Branford, Boston, 1954. This book describes various methods of propagating plants at home or in the garden.

Climates in Miniature, by T. Bedford Franklin, Philosophical Library, New York, 1955.   This book explains how you can make a study of the effects of soil differences, sunlight, temperature, and humidity on small plots of ground. It suggests many useful experiments for individual research.

How to Know the Protozoa, by T. L. Jahn, Wm. C. Brown, Dubuque, Ia., 1949.   This is a guide to the identification of many of the protozoa which one is likely to encounter in microscope work.

Handbook of Nature Study, 24th edition, by Anna B. Comstock, Comstock Publishing Co., Ithaca, N.Y. (undated).

Fieldbook of Natural History, by E. Lawrence Palmer, Whittlesey House, McGraw-Hill, New York, 1949.
No single book can cover all of natural history, but these two books will help the amateur naturalist identify many of the plants, animals, and rocks that he may run across in his collecting.

Drosophila Guide, 5th edition, by Demerec and Kaufman, Carnegie Institution of Washington, Washington, D.C., 1950.   This pamphlet is a must for any boy or girl who is carrying on experiments in heredity with Drosophila flies. It describes how to culture the flies, and it has an appendix containing a series of experiments for the beginner. It provides excellent material for project work.

About Mice and Man, by Frederick R. Avis, J. Weston Walch, Box 1075, Portland, Me., 1957.   An excellent laboratory manual on the mouse as an animal for research. It includes information on care and feeding, directions for building cages and other apparatus; describes the life cycle and the reproductive cycle of the mouse; deals with anatomy, surgery, tumors, tissue culture, and genetics.

Practical Taxidermy, by John W. Moyer, Ronald Press, New York, 1953. If your project involves stuffing and mounting animals, this book will help. It describes the basic techniques required, and there are many illustrations to help the amateur understand clearly the steps in the process.

How to Make Good Pictures, Eastman Kodak, Rochester, N.Y., 1951.
Photography Through the Microscope, Eastman Kodak, Rochester, N.Y., 1952.
Many projects require some camera work. These books will give you whatever information you may need for this.

Clinical Diagnosis by Laboratory Methods, 12th edition, by James C. Todd *et al.,* Saunders, Philadelphia, 1953.   If your project involves the study of blood, urine, or other physiological aspects or activities of the body, the techniques you need will probably be found in this book. It is a standard reference work in this field.

Practical Physiological Chemistry, 12th edition, by P. B. Hawk *et al.,* Blakiston, McGraw-Hill, New York, 1947.
Principles and Methods of Chemical Analysis, by Harold F. Walton, Prentice-Hall, Englewood Cliffs, N.J., 1952.
These two books will be useful if your project requires chemical analysis. They give data on reagents, procedures, techniques.

Paper Chromatography — A Laboratory Manual, by Richard J. Block *et al.,* Academic Press, New York, 1952.   This manual outlines the procedures to be followed in analyzing substances by paper chromatography.
The Care and Handling of Glass Volumetric Apparatus, Kimble Glass Co., Toledo, Ohio (undated).   This is a beautifully done booklet of about 20 pages, profusely illustrated with excellent diagrams and graphs. The booklet outlines for the beginner how to use, care for, calibrate, and extend the life of pieces of volumetric glassware, such as pipettes and burettes, that are used in the laboratory.
Handbook of Chemistry and Physics, Charles Hodgman (editor), Chemical Rubber Company, Cleveland, Ohio, 1945.   This standard reference work is a source of much information which may be useful in projects dealing with chemistry and physics.

Laboratory Manual for Radio and Television Technicians — Book I, Basic Electricity; Book II, Basic Electronics; Book III, Basic Radio and Radio Receiver Servicing; Book IV, Basic Television and Television Receiver Servicing — by Paul B. Zbar and Sid Schildkraut (Teaching Staff, Radio-Electronics-Television Manufacturers' Association), McGraw-Hill, New York, 1956 and 1958.
Techniques in Experimental Electronics, by C. H. Bachman, Wiley, New York, 1948.

Radio Amateur's Handbook, 9th edition, by Archie F. Collins, Crowell, New York, 1949.

Procedures in Experimental Physics, by John Strong *et al.,* Prentice-Hall, Englewood Cliffs, N.J., 1938.

These books and manuals outline fundamental procedures in certain areas of physics. They describe how to construct apparatus for testing phenomena which may be involved in your project. Experiments are described.

Making and Using a Telescope, by H. P. Wilkins and P. A. Moore, McClelland, 1956.

Exploring the Universe, by R. A. Gallant, Garden City Books, Doubleday, Garden City, N.Y., 1956.

Together, these two books (the second written especially for boys and girls) will serve as adequate preparation for observing the heavens.

Techniques of Observing the Weather, by B. C. Haynes, Wiley, New York, 1947.   This book describes the instruments and the methods which are used for making weather observations.

Field Guide to Rocks and Minerals, 2nd edition, by Frederick H. Pough, Houghton Mifflin, Boston, 1955.

Guide to the Study of Rocks, by Leslie E. Spock, Harper, New York, 1953.

These books will be of use to anyone whose project requires the identification of rocks or minerals in the field.

7. Where to Get Ideas for Building and Displaying Your Project.

Science Exhibits, Science Clubs of America, Washington, D.C.

Here you can find how to plan and select materials for an exhibit, plus information on displaying the materials, labeling the exhibit, and the use of lighting effects.

How to Make a Home Nature Museum, by Vinson Brown, Little, Brown, Boston, 1954.   This book describes how to make a display and set it off to best advantage.

How to Make a Miniature Zoo, by Vinson Brown, Little, Brown, Boston, 1956.   If your project deals with living organisms, this book may prove to be helpful in preparing the display. It deals with the collection of insects, fish, amphibia, reptiles, birds, and mammals — how to cage them, care for them, and display them either inside or outside.

Making Posters, Flashcards, and Charts, by Gertrude L. Power, U.S. Dept. of Agriculture, Federal Extension Service, Misc. Pub. No. 796, Washington, D.C., Oct. 1956.   A pamphlet of about 20 pages giving many useful hints on the preparation of charts and graphs. It is intended for extension teaching, but the ideas are applicable to the preparation of displays for science fairs or science congresses.

Lettering for Extension Visual Aids, by Gertrude L. Power, U.S. Dept. of Agriculture, Federal Extension Service, Agriculture Handbook No. 22, Washington, D.C., 1951.   A 12 page pamphlet with many valuable suggestions on lettering, for the preparation of posters, charts, and displays. The ideas presented may be very helpful in the preparation of an exhibit for a science fair or science congress.

8. Where to Find Suggestions for Improving Your Written or Oral Report.

The Way to Write, by R. F. Flesch and A. H. Lass, McGraw-Hill, New York, 1955.   This is actually a textbook for high school pupils. It has much valuable information on how to organize your report and write it in readable form.

" The Principles of Poor Writing," by Paul W. Merril, *Scientific Monthly*, Jan. 1947, pp. 72–74.   This short article is written in sarcastic vein. It outlines many of the faults of poor writing.

Scientific Writing, by M. R. Emberger and M. R. Hall, Harcourt, Brace, New York, 1955.   Here is an excellent reference book on how to write a scientific article or report. It is intended for the college student, but there is much here that a high school student can use with profit. Perhaps the most valuable part is the section in which several scientific reports are reprinted in whole or in part, and analyzed for style of presentation.

The Underwater Zoo, by Theodore McClintock, Vanguard, New York, 1938 (out of print).   Check with your school or public librarian to see if one of these libraries has a copy of this book. It is a journal, illustrated by the author, describing his observations on certain aquatic animals which he collected with a soup strainer from a pond. It shows what a nonscientist can do with simple equipment. The book is written in the form of a dated log, and is illustrated with line drawings. The simplicity of the style can serve as a model for the record kept by a high school pupil.

How to Communicate Ideas, by Richard Borden, Economics Press, Inc., P.O. Box 460, Montclair, N.J. (undated).
A 20 page booklet which gives in interesting form a series of suggestions for making a good speech. While the booklet refers to speaking only, the same ideas are actually applicable to writing a good report.

9. In Case You Need More Information About Statistics —

Graphic Presentation, by Willard C. Brinton, Brinton Associates, New York, 1939 (out of print).   This is a manual which describes the use of graphs and charts as aids in presenting data of various kinds. Check your school and public libraries for a copy.

Elementary Statistics with General Applications, by Morris M. Blair, Holt, New York, 1944.

Elementary Statistics, by H. E. Garrett, Longmans, New York, 1956.

Statistical Methods Applied to Experiments in Agriculture and Biology, 5th edition, by G. W. Snedecor, Iowa State College Press, 1956.
The first two of these books are standard texts of general statistics. The third concerns the use of statistics in biological experiments.

How to Lie with Statistics, by Darrell Huff, Norton, New York, 1954.
A small book which explains in readable form how statistics can be used to say anything which the user wants them to say. The book cites actual cases of misuse of statistics in advertising and business, as well as in propaganda. It is well illustrated with cartoon drawings. By studying the ways in which statistics can be made to lie, you can learn what *not to do* when using statistics in a scientific report.

Index

Page numbers in **bold** type indicate illustrations.

projects, 56–63, 73, 100; defined, 56–57; characteristics of good, 60–63

Pythagoras, 11, 14

r

range, 169

Readers' Guide to Periodical Literature, 84–86

reading a paper, 151–159, **152, 153.** *See also* reporting the results (oral report)

readings, locating preliminary, 83–88; dangers of, 83–84; values of, 84, 89; recording, 89–91, **90, 91;** importance of recording, 83, 89; methods of recording, 89–91, **90, 91;** sources of, 84–88, 183–189

recording, importance of recording observations, 101, 102; accuracy of record, 108–111. *See also* tables

Redi, Francesco, 15–19, **17,** 37; experiment described, 15–18, **17,** 43–44

reliability, measures of, 127, 179–181

Remsen, Ira, 71–72

reports, of results, 138–139; criteria for judging quality of, 143–144; sample of, 145–150, **146, 147, 148;** oral, 151–159, **152, 153;** written, 140–144; what to include in, 140–142

Richet, Charles, 49–50, 56

Roentgen, William, 26, 49, 56

s

Salk, Jonas, 45–46, **45**

scattergram (scatter diagram), 174, **175, 176,** 177, **178**

science, defined, 8; accomplishments in, 160–162, **161;** language of, 139. *See also* scientific methods

science congress, 151–159, **152, 153**

science fairs, described, 57–59; sample criteria used for judging entries, 62–63

scientific methods, 7, 8–24, **13, 17, 21,** 56, 72; summarized, 9–10; use in solving problems, 10, 11–24

serendipity, 47–51; defined, 47; origin of word, 47

significant figures, 110–111

Snow, John, 30

Spallanzani, Lazaro, 20, 118, 140, 141

standard deviation, 171–173, **172**

standard error, 181

statistics, 163–182, **165, 166, 167, 168, 170, 172, 175, 176, 178, 179;** defined, 127; measures of central tendency, 163–167 (mean, 163–164, 167, **172,** 173; median, 163, 164–165, **165,** 167; mode, 163, 165–166, **166,** 167); measures of variability, 167–173 (range, 169; average deviation, 169–171, **172;** standard deviation, 171, 173); measures of correlation, 173–179; measures of reliability, 179–182 (probable error, 180–181, standard error, 181, what reliability does not mean, 181–182). *See also* significant figures, graphs, tables

Steinberg, Bernhard, 131

t

tables, 101, 112–116; sample tables, **107, 113, 115, 116,** 167, **168, 170, 172, 175, 176, 178**

techniques, importance of learning in advance, 92–93; recording, 90–91, **90, 91,** 93; references for, 186–188

Tombaugh, Clyde W., 22

trial and error, 33–36; defined, 33

Tyndall, John, 20

u

" Useless " ideas. *See* applications

v

variability, measures of, 127, 167–173, **168, 170, 172,** 179

Vesalius, Andreas, 26

Von Mehring, 50

w

Waksman, Selman A., 35

Walpole, Horace, 47

Withering, William, 35–36